A Beautiful Day
in the Neighborhood

The Poetry of Mister Rogers

Lyrics by
FRED ROGERS

Illustrations by
LUKE FLOWERS

QUIRK BOOKS
PHILADELPHIA

Contents

My name is Mister Rogers.

I'm glad that you are near.

You've made this day a special day

By just your being here.

—From the opening song of the Canadian show *Misterogers*,
the precursor of *Mister Rogers' Neighborhood*

Welcome to the Neighborhood

Won't You Be My Neighbor?

It's a beautiful day in this neighborhood
A beautiful day for a neighbor.
Would you be mine?
Could you be mine?

It's a neighborly day in this beauty wood
A neighborly day for a beauty.
Would you be mine?
Could you be mine?

I have always wanted to have a neighbor just like you!
I've always wanted to live in a neighborhood with you,
    So . . .

Let's make the most of this beautiful day
Since we're together, we might as well say
Would you be mine?
Could you be mine?

Won't you be my neighbor?
Won't you please,
Won't you please?
Please won't you be my neighbor?

Mister Rogers' Invitation

Would you like to meet the tiger
Who lives there in that clock?
Or see that Eiffel Tower
And hear a French man talk?

Would you like to use a telephone?
It's a tin can on a string
That lets you reach the castle
Where a most majestic king
His Majesty King Friday
    is in charge of everything!

Would you like to ride a trolley
Along that trolley track?
Or crawl right through the underpass—
Right through and then right back?

Then pop into this house here,
Come in and visit me.
There's lots for us to see and hear
And think and do and feel and be.

My name is Mister Rogers.
I'm glad that you are near.
You've made this day a special day
By just your being here.

Be the Best of Whatever You Are

If you can't be a pine
On the top of a hill
Be a shrub in the valley, but be
The best little shrub by the side of the rill.

If you can't be a woods
Be a tree.
If you can't be a highway
Then just be a trail.
If you can't be the sun
Be a star.

It isn't by size that you win or you fail.
Be the best of whatever you are.
Be the best of whatever you are!

I Like You as You Are

I like you as you are
Exactly and precisely!
I think you turned out nicely
And I like you as you are.

I like you as you are
Without a doubt or question
Or even a suggestion
'Cause I like you as you are.

I like your disposition
Your facial composition
And with your kind permission
I'll shout it to a star.

I like you as you are
I wouldn't want to change you
Or even rearrange you
Not by far.

I like you, I-L-I-K-E-Y-O-U.
I like you, yes I do,
I like you, Y-O-U.
I like you, like you as you are.

Lyrics by Josie Carey, Music by Fred Rogers

I Think I'm Going to Like Today

I think I'm going to like today
I think I'll call it fine
I'll wrap it in ribbons
And make it mine.

I think I'm going to like today
It's very plain to see
I like every minute
And it likes me.

18

Don't you agree?
This is the nicest day in the neighborhood
The nicest day in the calendar
The nicest day in the hemisphere for me.

I think I'm going to like today
It's been the best by far.
I got it by wishing
On last night's star.

I think I'm going to like today
And when today is through
I'll catch it and keep it
As good as new.

I'll have the nicest day in the neighborhood
The nicest day in the calendar
The nicest day will just stay at home with me.
I think I'm going to like today.

I Give a Hoot for You

Oh, I give a hoot for you
'Cause golly, you're neat!
Yes, I give a hoot for you
You simply couldn't be beat.

You're nice as pie and really, I
Don't know when, why, or what!
But I've got to say, that in every way,
You're my "fa-vo-rut."

Oh, I give a hoot for you
You're swell, that's how I feel!
Yes, I give a hoot for you
You're absolutely for real.

I'm hoping, too, as I hoot for you
That you will soon agree
To hoot and howl like this wise old owl
And give a hoot for me: "Hoot!"

Lyrics by Josie Carey, Music by Fred Rogers

Children Can

Who can crawl under a table?
Who can sit under a chair?
Who can fit their feet in little shoes
And sleep most anywhere?
Who can play very much longer
Play much harder than grownups ever dare?
You're a child so you can do it.
You can do it anywhere!

Who can wake up every morning
And be ready right away?
Who can notice all the tiny things
That other people say?
Who can make the things they play with
Something different for every single day?
You're a child and you can do it.
You can do it any way!

Roll in the grass
Squoosh in the mud
Lick an ice cream cone
Sing to a bass
Splash in a flood
By a stepping stone . . .
    all alone.

Who can put your hand in my hand
And be ready to feel all safe and strong?
You're a child so you can do it.
Children do it all life long!

It's Good to Talk

It's good to talk
It's good to say the things we feel
It's good to talk.
We're much more real without the lot.

It's good to talk
It's good to find someone to trust
It's good to talk.
We know we must do more than balk.

People weren't born to be silent
Our tongues make wonderful sounds.
Just try a few phrases for practice
You'll see there are very few bounds.

Let's see now: "I like you. I'm angry.
I'm happy. I'm sad."
You see? That's not bad.
It's good, not bad.

It's good to talk.
It's good to say the things we mean.
It's good to talk of all we've seen and heard and felt for
And wished and knelt for.

We need to talk more.
It's good to talk.

Things Are Different

You never know the story
By the cover of the book.
You can't tell what a dinner's like
By simply looking at the cook.
It's something everybody needs to know
Way down deep inside
That things are often different
Than the way they look.

When I put on a costume
To play a fancy part
That costume changes just my looks.
It doesn't change my heart.
You cannot know what someone's thinking
By the picture you just took
'Cause things are often different
From the way they look.

A Place of My Own

I like to have a place of my own
A place where I can be by myself.
When I want to think and play by myself
I like to have a place of my own.

I like to have a place of my own
A step on a staircase, a drawer or a chair,
A corner, a spot anywhere,
A place I can call my own.

Dishes have places
So do pots and pans
Beds and bathtubs
Shoes and socks.

Tables have places
So do faces and hands.
Houses have places
Keys have locks.

I like to have a place of my own
A place where I can be by myself.
When I want to play and think by myself
I like to have a place of my own.

Smile in Your Pocket

There's a smile in your pocket
There's a smile up your sleeve
There's a smile in your pocket
And it isn't make-believe.

There's a smile in your pocket
There's a smile in your shoe
There's a smile in your pocket
Without anything to do.

Now, a pocket is handy for candy
    And dandy for string.
A pocket is nifty for folks who are thrifty
With wrappers and rings—
All sorts of things.

But a smile in your pocket
Feels a bit out of place
'Cause a smile in your pocket
Wants to be on your face!

Lyrics by Josie Carey, Music by Fred Rogers

You Are You

I eat and you do, too.
You sleep and I do, too.
I wake up and you do, too.
So we two do so much the same—
But I'm Mister Rogers
And you have your name.

You are you and I am I
And we will always be
Quite different to people who know us well
'Cause they're the ones who like us to be different.

You are you and I am I
And we will never be
Exactly like anybody else
'Cause everybody else is different.
Different, different, we are different.
Isn't it great?
To be different!

You and I and he and she
    And isn't it great to be you and I?
And we will always be
Quite different to people who know us well.
'Cause they're the ones who like us
They really want us
They're the ones who like us to be different.

What Do You Do with the Mad That You Feel?

What do you do with the mad that you feel
When you feel so mad you could bite?
When the whole wide world seems oh so wrong
And nothing you do seems very right?

What do you do? Do you punch a bag?
Do you pound some clay or some dough?
Do you round up friends for a game of tag?
Or see how fast you go?

It's great to be able to stop
When you've planned a thing that's wrong
And be able to do something else instead
And think this song:

I can stop when I want to
Can stop when I wish
I can stop, stop, stop anytime.
And what a good feeling to feel like this
And know that the feeling is really mine.

Know that there's something deep inside
That helps us become what we can.
For a girl can be someday a woman
And a boy can be someday a man.

I Love to Shine

I love to shine, I love to shine
I love to let what's in me
 Shine outside.
I love to shine, I love to shine
I love to let what's in me
 Shine outside.

The world needs all the light
 That we can muster
Each moon and star and comet
 In the sky.

We add to all the world
    Our special luster
So shine on, friends,
    And never question why.

We love to shine,
    We love to shine
We love to let what's in us
    Shine outside.
We love to let what's in us
    Shine outside.

Fences

Fences, fences, the world is full of fences
And some I like
And some I don't like
That keep me out.
Now the kind that keep me out
Are the kind that make me pout.
They're the kind that have no gate at all.
They're the kind that go up too tall.

Fences, fences, the world is full of fences
And some I like.
Yes, some I do like.
The kind that keep me safe.
Now, the kind that keep me safe, you see
Are the kind that keep wild beasts from me.
They're the kind that help me stop my car
So I never have to go too far.

Fences, fences, the world is full of fences.
From what I see
They're a help to me.
And the ones I hate
I can tolerate.
So, fences, fences
The world must keep its

many

many

fences.

Doing Song

Clap your hands
Blow a kiss
Make a face
Like this!

Snap your thumbs
Shake your head
Make-believe
You're in bed.

Blink your eyes
Stretch your arms
Stand up straight
Look for farms.

Here's the horse (*Neigh!*)
Here's the cow (*Moooo!*)
Here's the sheep (*Baaaa!*)
You can bow.

Here's the duck (*Quack quack!*)
Here's the cat (*Meow!*)
Here's the dog (*Bark!*)
Here's your hat.

Wave goodbye
Drive the car
Throw the ball
Throw it far.

Eat your meal
Sing a song
Brush your teeth
Hear ding-dong!

Hug your pillow
Click the light
Hug yourself
Say goodnight. (*Goodnight!*)

Les Jours de la Semaine
(The Days of the Week)

In France the days are just the same,
    The same as over here.
The sun goes up and then comes down
Each week and month and year.

But since the French speak differently
Their days don't sound the same.
What say we learn it their way?
I think that would be tame.

The first day is *Lundi*
Monday's what we say.
The next day is *Mardi*
In English that's Tuesday.

Wednesday is *Mercredi*.
    Then *Jeudi* comes your way.
What's the French for Friday?
Vendredi, they say.

The weekend starts with *Samedi*.
That's Saturday, you know.
Dimanche is French for Sunday.
    Where did that whole week go?

Lundi, Mardi, Mercredi, Jeudi,
    Vendredi, Samedi, Dimanche.
That's fun, don't you agree?

Lyrics by Josie Carey, Music by Fred Rogers

39

Take My Time

I like to take my time.
I mean that when I want to do a thing
I like to take my time to do it right.
I mean I might just make mistakes
If I should have to hurry up.

And so I like to take my time
To tie my shoes, to eat, to get dressed
To go to sleep at night, to sing a song for you
And everything I like to do.

I like to take my time.
I mean that when I want to do a thing
I like to take my time to do it well.
I mean I might just make mistakes
If I should have to hurry up and so
I like to take my time.

What Can You Hear?

What can you hear
    When you close your eyes
When you close your eyes
    And listen a while.
Can you hear? Can you hear?

Can you hear the love, the anger, the joy
The sadness, the fear?
Can you hear the whisper of someone
    Who wants to be very near?

What can you hear
        When you close your eyes?

Can you hear

            a birdie

        singing a song

    in the skies?

    Can you hear?

I'm Busy Being Busy

I'm busy being busy
Yes, the calendar's my task.
I'm busy giving dates away
To all who come and ask
For a week for this, a week for that.

I'm busy being busy
And the busier I get
The more some people need a week
For barbershop quartets, and a week
For tuna fish croquettes.

I found a week for cheddar cheese
For fleas and Spanish onions.
I found a week for willow trees
And bees and curing bunions.
I searched with purple passion
For a national event
Calling the world's attention
To the day the pretzel first was bent.

And I gave a special Groundhog's Day
To please dear Punxsutawney.
I gave a week to Turtle Creek,
A day to sing of Swanee.
I made a special leap year, too
And a day for wearing navy blue.
Oh, you'll never know how much I do
I'm busy being busy.

I'm busy being busy
And the busier I am
The more some people need a week
For elderberry jam, or a week
For naming babies Sam.

I'm busy being busy
And the busier I seem
The more I'm called upon to give
A day to sour cream, or a week
To pantomime
Or bells that chime
I don't have time
To even end this rhyme.
I'm very busy!

Lyrics by Josie Carey, Music by Fred Rogers

I Did, Too

Did you ever fall and hurt your hand or knee?
Did you ever bite your tongue?
Did you ever find the stinger of a bee
Stuck in your thumb?
I did, too.

It seems the things that you do
I did, too
When I was very new.
I had lots of hurts and scares and worries
When I was growing up like you.

Did you ever trip and fall down on the stairs?
Did you ever stub your toe?
Did you ever dream of great big grizzly bears
Who wouldn't go?
I did, too.

It seems the things that you do
I did, too
When I was very new.
I had lots of hurts and scares and worries
When I was growing up like you.

Sometimes Isn't Always

Sometimes I DON'T feel like combing my hair.
I DON'T feel like washing my face sometimes.
Sometimes I DON'T feel like saying "okay."
But sometimes isn't always.

Sometimes I DO feel like combing my hair.
I DO feel like washing my face sometimes.
Sometimes I DO feel like saying "okay."
But sometimes isn't always.

Sometimes I DON'T feel like going to bed.
I DO feel like getting right up sometimes.
Sometimes I DON'T feel like wearing my shoes.
But sometimes isn't always.

Sometimes I DON'T feel like sometimes I DO.
I feel like I DON'T like to feel sometimes.
Sometimes I DON'T . . . and sometimes I DO.
But sometimes isn't always
Isn't always
Isn't always.

Everybody's Shy Sometimes

Did you ever feel so shy
You thought you'd hide
You thought you'd hide
Beside your mom
Beside your dad?

Did you ever feel so shy
You wondered why
You wondered why
You didn't cry
You just felt shy?

Everyone feels a little shy sometimes
Even if you're big and tall.
Everyone thinks a little shy sometimes.
Everyone feels a little small sometimes.
Everyone feels a little shy.

I'd Like to Be Like Mom and Dad

I'd like to be just like my mom
She's loving and she's bright.
She knows just how to care for me
And works to make things right.

And Daddy likes the things she does
The way she looks, and gee!
I'd like to be just like my mom
And have someone like me.

I'd like to be just like my dad
He's wise and he is kind.
He knows just how to help me grow
And does his work just fine.

And Mommy likes the things he does
The way he looks, and gee!
I'd like to be just like my dad
And have someone like me.

You Can Never Go Down the Drain

You can never go down
Can never go down
Can never go down the drain.

You're bigger than the water.
You're bigger than the soap.
    You're much bigger than all the

                    b u b b l e s.

So you see . . .

You can never go down

Can never go down

the drain!

You can never go down

Can never go down

The Clown in Me

A clown, a clown
I think I'll be a clown.
I think I'll make the people laugh
And laugh all over town.
A clown, that's what I'll be. A clown!

Sometimes I feel when I'm afraid
That I will never make the grade.
So I pretend I'm someone else
And show the world my other self.
I'm not quite sure of me, you see
When I have to make a clown of me.

A clown, a clown
I think I'll be a clown.
I think I'll make the people laugh
And laugh all over town.
A clown, that's what I'll be. A clown!

Sometimes I feel all good inside
And haven't got a thing to hide.
My friends all tell me I'm the best
They think I'm better than the rest.
It's times like this I act myself
And I let the clown stay on the shelf.

Myself, myself
I think I'll be myself.
I think I'll let the people see
The comfortable inside of me.
Myself . . . I'll be myself!

It's only when I feel let down
I might be scared into a clown.
But he can be himself
When I can be . . .
Myself, myself
I think I'll be myself!

We Are Elephants

You can tell at once
We are elephants.
We are elephants big and strong.
From the backs and fronts
We are elephants.
We're elephants all day long.

From the tip of the tusk to the knee
We are elephantinus as can be.
From the trunks to our tails you can see
We're a ponderous, prosperous,
     pompous, preposterous
Pachyderm family of three.

You can smell at once
We are elephants.
We are elephants, come what may.
And we yell at once:
"We are elephants!
And it's elephants we will stay!"

Summer Rain

The sun is sad and I am glad
My flower has needed the rain.
The summer sky's been awfully dry
My flower just had to complain.

I know it's wet as it can get
But listen and let me explain:
If you were a flower
You'd wish for a shower—
A lovely summer rain.

My flower's bed was hard as lead
Before we had this summer rain.
My flower's head was bowed and red
I think she had cause to complain.

And then the sky began to cry
And water poured down once again.
Although we are wetter
My flower feels better—
She loves the summer rain.

It's an Ugly Day

It's an ugly day
Made of mugly gray
It's a sit-down-by-the-fire
And be snuggly day.

It's a cloudy day
And a dowdy day
It's a play-some-Chinese-checkers
Read-out-loud day.

It's a day to cuddle up
With a chocolate cookie
Hook a rug or knit—
'Cause it's an ugly day
Made of mugly gray
It's a better-wear-your-sweater
And be snuggly day.

If we pop us some corn
And have cinnamon toast
I'd say we'd made the most
Of an ugly day.

I'm Glad I'm the Way I Am

I'm glad I'm the way I am
I'm glad I'm me.
I'm glad I'm the way
That I'm supposed to be.

I like how I look
I like the way that I feel
I feel that I have a right to be
Quite pleased with me.

I'm glad I'm the way I am
I think I'm fine.
I'm glad I'm the way I am
The pleasure's mine.

It's good that I look the way I should
Wouldn't change now if I could
'Cause I'm happy to be me!

Walking Giraffe

I love to take my giraffe
for walks

He's taller
than anyone else
I know.

You're welcome to talk
with my
tall giraffe

He's kind
from his head
to his toe.

So step up
and speak to
my pet giraffe,

He'll talk to us down
here below.

I'm Still Myself Inside

I can put on a hat or put on a coat
Or wear a pair of glasses or sail in a boat.
I can change all my names
And find a place to hide.
I can do almost anything but
I'm still myself inside.

I can go far away or dream anything
Or wear a scary costume or act like a king.
I can change all my names
And find a place to hide.
I can do almost anything but
I'm still myself
I'm still myself
I'm still myself inside.

Everything Grows Together

Everything grows together

Because you're all one piece.

Your toes grow

As your feet grow

As your legs grow

As your fingers grow

As your hands grow

As your arms grow

As your ears grow

As your nose grows

As the rest of you grows

Because you're all one piece!

It Hurts to Be Lonely

It hurts so much to be lonely
And there's no one else around.
There's no one who really cares for me
Nowhere to be found.

Oh, what I'd give for another chance
Now that I know I was wrong.
And wouldn't it be simply wonderful
If someone came along who knows
It hurts so much to be lonely.

Oh how happy I could be
If that special someone held my hand
And said, "Come, be with me."
It hurts so much to be lonely.
Oh, how life can be so cruel
But I only have myself to blame.
Why was I such a fool?

Oh what I'd give for another chance
Now that I know I was wrong.
And wouldn't it be simply wonderful
If someone came along who knows
It hurts so much to be lonely.

Oh, how happy I could be
If that special someone held my hand
And said, "Come, be with me."

Are You Brave?

Are you brave and don't know it?
Are you brave and can't tell?
Are you brave and just don't show it
While others know it very well?

Are you brave and you wonder?
Are you brave and you doubt?
Are you brave above and under
Especially when you're inside out?

Tell me,
Won't you tell me?
Tell me,
Are you brave?

Parents Were Little Once, Too

It's great for me to remember
As I put away my toys
That mothers were all little girls one time
And fathers were all little boys.

My daddy seems so big right now
He must have grown a lot.
Imagine how he felt one day
When he was just a tot.

My mother's not so big as Dad
But bigger than my sister.
I wonder if she ever had
A little fever blister.

It's great for me to remember
As I put away my toys
That mothers were all little girls one time
And fathers were all little boys.

Did You Know?

Did you know? Did you know?
Did you know that it's all right to wonder?
Did you know that it's all right to wonder?
There are all kinds of wonderful things!

Did you know? Did you know?
Did you know that it's all right to marvel?
Did you know that it's all right to marvel?
There are all kinds of marvelous things!

You can ask a lot of questions about the world
And your place in it.
You can ask about people's feelings;
You can learn the sky's the limit.

Did you know? Did you know?
Did you know when you wonder you're learning?
Did you know when you marvel you're learning?
About all kinds of wonderful,
About all kinds of marvelous,
Marvelously wonderful things?

It's You I Like

It's you I like.
It's not the things you wear
It's not the way you do your hair
But it's you I like.

The way you are right now
The way down deep inside you
Not the things that hide you
Not your toys
They're just beside you.

But it's you I like.
Every part of you
Your skin, your eyes, your feelings
Whether old or new.

I hope that you'll remember
Even when you're feeling blue
That it's you I like
It's you yourself
It's you—

It's you I like!

What Do You Think Is Important?

What, what, what do you think
What do you think is important? (Really.)
What, what, what do you think
What do you think really counts?

What do you think about other people?
What do you think about new ideas?
What, what, what do you think
What do you think is important?

Some people think that houses and cars
And lots of fancy toys
Are things that are most important
For grown-up girls and boys.

Of course, houses are nice if there's love inside
And cars are, too, if they run well.
It's the things that we do with the toys that we have
That help us to feel that we've done well.

What, what, what do you think
What do you think is important? (Really.)
What, what, what do you think
What do you think is the best?

What kind of world would you like to live in?
What kind of love would you like to give?
What is essential for you and your neighbor?
What, what, what do you think
What do you think is important?

Many Ways to Say I Love You

There are many ways to say "I love you."
There are many ways to say "I care about you."
Many ways, many ways, many ways to say
"I love you."

There's the cooking way to say "I love you."
There's the cooking something someone really likes to eat.
The cooking way, the cooking way, the cooking way to say
"I love you."

There's the eating way to say "I love you."
There's the eating something someone made especially.
The eating way, the eating way, the eating way to say
"I love you."

Cleaning up a room can say "I love you."
Hanging up a coat before you're asked to.
Drawing special pictures for the holidays and
Making plays.

There are many ways to say "I love you."
Just by being there when things are sad and scary, just by
Being there, being there, being there to say
"I love you."

You'll find many ways to say "I love you."
You'll find many ways to understand what love is.
Many ways, many ways, many ways to say
"I love you."

Cooking, eating
Cleaning, drawing
Playing, being
Understanding
Love you.

Please Don't Think It's Funny

Sometimes you feel like holding your pillow all night long.
Sometimes you hug your teddy bear tightly
He's old but he's still strong.
And sometimes you want to snuggle up closely
With your own mom and dad.
At night, you even need the light sometimes
But that's not bad.

Please don't think it's funny
When you want an extra kiss.
There are lots and lots of people
Who sometimes feel like this.
Please don't think it's funny
When you want the ones you miss.
There are lots and lots of people
Who sometimes feel like this.

It's great to know you're growing up bigger every day.
But somehow things you like to remember
Are often put away.
And sometimes you wonder over and over
If you should stay inside.
When you enjoy a younger toy
You never need to hide.

In the long, long trip of growing
There are stops along the way
For thoughts of all the soft things
And a look at yesterday.

For a chance to fill our feelings
With comfort and with ease
And then tell the new tomorrow
"You can come now when you please."

So please don't think it's funny
When you want an extra kiss.
There are lots and lots of people
Who sometimes feel like this.
Please don't think it's funny
When you want the ones you miss.
There are lots and lots of people
Who sometimes feel like this.

Let's Be Together Today

Let's go right away, go somewhere today
Let's be together and stay and stay.
Let's go together today, right away.
Let's be together today!

Together's the way I like the best.
I like to be with you.
I like the things you explain to me—
The things you show me to do.

Let's go right away, go somewhere today
Let's be together and stay and stay.
Let's go together today.

Right away, let's be together today.

Some days it's good to play alone
But sometimes I get bored.
There's just so much you can do yourself
With a ball or a doll or a sword.

But whenever I hear you've got some time
And want me to be with you,
I wonder how you knew
'Cause that's what I wanted, too!

Let's go right away, go somewhere today

Let's be together and stay and stay.

Let's go together today right away.

Let's be together today!

You're Growing

You used to creep and crawl real well
But then you learned to walk real well.
There was a time you'd coo and cry
But then you learned to talk, and, my!
You hardly ever cry
You hardly ever crawl at all
I like the way you're growing up.
It's fun! That's all!

You're growing, you're growing
You're growing in and out.
You're growing, you're growing
You're growing all about.

Your hands are getting bigger now.
Your arms and legs are longer now.
You even sense your insides grow
When Mom and Dad refuse you, so
You're learning how to wait now.
It's great to hope and wait somehow.
I like the way you're growing up.
It's fun! That's all!

You're growing, you're growing
You're growing in and out.
You're growing, you're growing
You're growing all about.

Your friends are getting bigger now.
They're better every day somehow.
You used to stay at home to play
But now you even play away.
You do important things now.
Your friends and you do big things now.
I like the way you're growing up.
It's fun! That's all!

You're growing, you're growing
You're growing in and out.
You're growing, you're growing
You're growing all about.

Someday you'll be a grown-up, too
And have some children grow up, too.
Then you can love them in and out
And tell them stories all about
The times when you were their size
The times when you found great surprise
In growing up. And they will sing:
"It's fun! That's all."

You're growing, you're growing
You're growing in and out.
You're growing, you're growing
You're growing all about.

Some Things
I Don't Understand

Some things I don't understand.
Some things are scary and sad.
Sometimes I even get bad when I'm mad.
Sometimes I even get glad.

Why does a dog have to bark?
Why does an elephant die?
Why can't we play all the time in the park?
Why can't my pussycat fly?
    Why,
          why,
  why,
        why,
              why,
           why?
                I wonder why.

Why do fire engines make noise?
Why is hot water so hot?
Why aren't live babies like my other toys?
Why do I wonder a lot?

Someday, oh someday, I'll know what to say.
Someday, oh someday, I'll not have to say
"Why?"

When a Baby Comes

When a baby comes to your house
It's a girl or it's a boy.
It's a sister or a brother,
But it's never just a toy.

It can cry and it can holler.
It can wet and it can coo.
But there's one thing it can never—
It can never be like you.

You were there before the baby.
Now the baby's always there.
Now you wait for special moments
With your mother in the chair.

You're a very special person.
You are special to your mom.
And your dad begins to say, "You'll
Always be the older one."

It's so good to know that always
There's a special place for you.
And a special place for baby
Right inside the family, too.

You've a place that no one else has.
There is only one like you.

The King and the Ocean

"I have a notion
To move to the ocean!"
Declared a king in his tower
After thinking for an hour.
He traveled for days around his land
But he couldn't find an ocean at hand.
Finally, the king returned to his tower.
He thought and thought for another hour,
Then said he so loud and clear
So all could hear,
"You know, I'm fond of my own pond.
I think I'll stay right here!"

Sometimes I Wonder If I'm a Mistake

Sung by Daniel Striped Tiger

Sometimes I wonder if I'm a mistake
I'm not like anyone else I know.
When I'm asleep or even awake
Sometimes I get to dreaming that
I'm just a fake.

I'm not like anyone else.
Others I know are big and are wild.
I'm very small and quite tame.
Most of the time I'm weak and I'm mild.
Do you suppose that's a shame?

Often I wonder if I'm a mistake.
I'm not supposed to be scared, am I?
Sometimes I cry and sometimes I shake
Wondering "Isn't it true
That the strong never break?"

I'm not like anyone else I know
I'm not like anyone else.

Sung by Lady Aberlin

I think you are just fine as you are.
I really must tell you
I do like the person that you are becoming.
When you are sleeping,
When you are waking,
You are my friend.
It's really true.
I like you.
Crying or shaking or dreaming or breaking
There's no one mistaking it!
You're my best friend.
You're not a fake.
You're no mistake.
You are my friend.

A Bird-Watching Song

I am the merry bird-watcher
I watch them through my telescope.
I watch them as they build their nests
And gather food and sing and rest.
I raise my telescope to my eyes
And watch the birds as they fly by.
And from this angle I can see
The birds as they fly merrily.

You Are Special

You are my friend,
You are special.
You are my friend,
You're special to me.

You are the only one like you.
Like you, my friend, I like you.
In the daytime
In the nighttime
Anytime that you feel's the right time
For a friendship with me, you see

F - R - I - E - N - D

special.

You are my friend,
You're special to me.
There's only one
In this wonderful world.

You
are
special.

Creation Duet

What made the rainbow and the sky?
What made the bird and let it fly?
What made the hour, what made the day?
What has the power to make the flower?
And what made the rain and made the snow?
Made us and made us want to know?

Love made the rainbow, the bird,
    and the summer sun.
Love made the mountain, the stars,
    each and every one.
Love made the sea and love made the land.
Love made the mighty
    and love made the very small.
Love made the world, made the people
Love made it all.

Lyrics by Josie Carey, Music by Fred Rogers

Who Shall I Be Today?

Who shall I be today, I say?
Who shall I be today, this day?
A dark horse, a light cow
A doggy or a cat.
A gray mouse, a blue owl
Or something like that.
There's so much to choose
And so much to be
That's why it's fun to be anybody.

Who shall I be today, I say?
Who shall I be today, this day?
A king or a queen
Or a doctor or a nurse.
A streetcar conductor, a witch with a curse.
There's so much to choose
And so much to be
That's why it's fun to be anybody.

One day I decided to be a fireman strong
I squirted water bravely and I rang
    the firehouse gong.
The next day was a Sunday so I
    most naturally
Just chose to be a singer
And I sang most gloriously.
Another day I baked a pie
Another wrote a book.
One day I was a fisherman
And fished without a hook.

Someday I'll be an engineer
Someday I'll dig a moat.
Someday I'll be a carpenter
Someday I'll drive a boat.
But . . .

Who shall I be today, I say?
Who shall I be today, this day?
A rich man, a poor man
A beggar man, a thief.
A doctor, a lawyer
A commander in chief.

There's so much to choose
And so much to be
That's why it's fun
To be anybody.
Anybody!

Good People Sometimes Do Bad Things

Good people sometimes think bad things,
Good people dream bad things
Don't you?
Good people even say bad things,
Once in a while we do.

Good people sometimes wish bad things,
Good people try bad things
Don't you?
Good people even do bad things,
Once in a while we do.

Has anybody said you're good lately?
Has anybody said you're nice?
And have you wondered how they could, lately,
Wondered once or twice?
    Did you forget that . . .

Good people sometimes feel bad things?
Good people want bad things
They do!
Good people even do bad things,
Once in a while we do.
Good people sometimes do!

You're Much More

You're not just your toes or your chin or your size
Not just a bit or a spot or a part
You're not just your outsides—
You're also your heart.

You see there's more than honking to geeses
And there's more to a cow than a moo.
When you add up all the pieces
There is more than we see to you.
When we put you all together
You're a beautiful, marvelous,
Spirited, lovely,
Wonderful one of a kind!

You're much more than your anger
And you're much more than your fist.
A closet's more than a hanger
And a fist has an arm and a wrist.
You're much more than your sadness
And you're much more than your frown.
More than a yell or a tap or a pout
More than a bellow or a slap or a doubt.
You're more than a moment, a feeling, a part,
You're more than an outside, you're inside your heart.

You're much much more than your anger
Much much more than your mind.
When they put you all together
You're a beautiful, marvelous, spirited, lovely,
Wonderful one of a kind!

I Need You

I need you so I can be your neighbor.
I need you so I can be your friend.
I need you so I can be who I am.
Who I am—I am your friend!

You need me so you can be my neighbor.
You need me so you can be my friend.
You need me so you can be who you are.
Who you are—you are my friend!

A bird needs air for its wings to fly.
A boat needs water to float.
A teacher needs students who want to know why.
An election needs a vote.
And a lining needs a coat.
Just as I need you so I can be who I am,
You need me so you can be yourself!

We both need each other
So we can be who we are.
Who we are—we are friends!

We both need each other
So we can be each other's—
We can be each other's friend.

I'm Interested in Things

I wish I could look inside the telephone.
I hear the voice, but I wish that I could see.
I'm interested in things like the telephone.
I'm interested in lots and lots of things.

I wish that I could look inside our trunk at home.
It's very old and I'm not supposed to look.
I'm interested in things like our trunk at home.
I'm interested in lots and lots of things.

I see the pictures in my book
And someday I'll know what the words all say.
If I wait long enough maybe I could cook.
Even hot things! Or drive the car or saw the wood
Or clean out the trunk or run the washing machine.
Someday I'll make my way okay.

Still, I wish that I could look inside big people's things.
Especially things that I'm not allowed to see.
I'm interested in all those big people things.
I'm interested in lots and lots of things.

But I can wait, and later on you'll see
I'll still be interested
always interested
In many things
In many, many things.

I Like to Be Told

I like to be told
When you're going away
When you're going to come back
And how long you will stay
How long you will stay
I like to be told.

I like to be told
If it's going to hurt
If it's going to be hard
If it's not going to hurt
I like to be told.

I like to be told
It helps me to get ready for all those things
All those things that are new.
I trust you more and more
Each time that I'm
Finding those things to be true.

I like to be told
'Cause I'm trying to grow
'Cause I'm trying to learn
And I'm trying to know.

I like to be told
I like to be told.

I Hope It Will Rain

I'm going to France in the morning.
I'm going by plane, by plane in the morning.
I hope it will rain 'cause I know how to say
Il pleut, it's raining, *il pleut*.

I'm going to Spain in the morning.
I'm going by plane, by plane in the morning.
I hope it will rain 'cause I know how to say
Está lloviendo, it's raining, *está lloviendo*.

I'm going to Germany in the morning.
I'm going by plane, by plane in the morning.
I hope it will rain 'cause I know how to say
Es regnet, it's raining, *es regnet*.

I'm going to Italy in the morning.
I'm going by plane, by plane in the morning.
I hope it will rain 'cause I know how to say
It's raining, *Piove*.

A Lonely Kind of Thing

It's a lonely thing
To think you might
Do something
That might make
    someone very mad.

It's a lonely thing
To think you might
Hurt someone
And that someone
Might be your mom or dad
Someone you like very much.

It's so lonely
Lonely
It's a very
    lonely,
    lonely

Kind of thing.

Sometimes People Are Good

Sometimes people are good
And they do just what they should.
But the very same people who are good sometimes
Are the very same people who are bad sometimes.
It's funny, but it's true.
It's the same, isn't it, for
Me and . . .

Sometimes people get wet
And their parents get upset.
But the very same people who get wet sometimes
Are the very same people who are dry sometimes.
It's funny, but it's true.
It's the same, isn't it, for
Me and . . .

Sometimes people make noise
And they break each other's toys.
But the very same people who are noisy sometimes
Are the very same people who are quiet sometimes.
It's funny, but it's true.
It's the same, isn't it, for
Me and . . .

Sometimes people get mad
And they feel like being bad.
But the very same people who are mad sometimes
Are the very same people who are glad sometimes.
It's funny, but it's true.
It's the same, isn't it, for
Me and . . .

Sometimes people are good
And they do just what they should.
But the very same people who are good sometimes
Are the very same people who are bad sometimes.
It's funny, but it's true.
It's the same, isn't it, for
Me . . . Isn't it the same for you?

I'm Tame

I don't growl anymore
I'm tame, I'm tame.
I don't prowl anymore
I'm tame.

I know right, I know wrong
I say thank you and please.
I remember to cover
My mouth when I sneeze.

I don't growl anymore
I'm tame, I'm tame.
I don't prowl anymore
I'm tame.

I use a napkin and fork
At each hamburger feast.
And act like a gentleman
Not like a beast.

I don't growl anymore
I'm tame, I'm tame.
I don't prowl anymore,
I'm tame.

Lyrics by Josie Carey, Music by Fred Rogers

Then Your Heart Is Full of Love

When your heart has butterflies inside it
Then your heart is full of love.
When your heart feels just like overflowing
Then your heart is full of love.

Love is fragile as your tears.
Love is stronger than your fears.
When your heart can sing another's gladness
Then your heart is full of love.

When your heart can cry another's sadness
Then your heart is full of love.
Love is fragile as your tears.
Love is stronger than your fears.

When your heart beats for a special someone
Then your heart is full of love.
When your heart has room for everybody
Then your heart is full of love.

Lyrics by Josie Carey, Music by Fred Rogers

The Truth Will Make Me Free

What if I were very, very sad
And all I did was smile?
I wonder after a while
What might become of my sadness?

What if I were very, very angry
And all I did was sit
And never think about it?
What might become of my anger?

Where would they go
And what would they do
If I couldn't let them out?
Maybe I'd fall, maybe get sick
Or doubt.

But what if I could know the truth
And say just how I feel?
I think I'd learn a lot that's real
About freedom.

I'm learning to sing a sad song when I'm sad.
I'm learning to say I'm angry when I'm very mad.
I'm learning to shout.
I'm getting it out!

I'm happy, learning
Exactly how I feel inside of me.
I'm learning to know the truth
I'm learning to tell the truth.
Discovering truth will make me free.

Wishes Don't Make Things Come True

One time I wished that a lion would come
And eat up my house and my street.
I was mad at the world and I wished that the beast
Would stomp everything with his big heavy feet
And eat everything with his big sharp teeth
And eat everything with his teeth.
But that wish certainly didn't come true
'Cause scary mad wishes don't make things come true.

One time I wished that a dragon would come
And burn up my Daddy's big store.
I was angry with him 'cause I wanted to play
And he went out the door to his store right away.
I wished that the dragon would burn his store,
I wished it would burn Daddy's store.
But that wish certainly didn't come true
'Cause scary mad wishes don't make things come true.

Everyone wishes for scary, mad things,
I'm sure that you sometimes do, too.
I've wished for so many and I can say
That all kinds of wishes are things just like play.
They're things that your thinking has made,
So wish them and don't be afraid.
I'm glad it's certainly that way, aren't you?
That scary mad wishes don't make things come true.
No kinds of wishes make things come true.

You've Got to Do It

You can make-believe it happens
Or pretend that something's true.
You can wish or hope or contemplate a thing you'd like to do.
But until you start to do it, you will never see it through.
'Cause the make-believe pretending just won't do it for you.
You've got to do it!

Every little bit, you've got to do it, do it, do it, do it.
And when you're through, you can know who did it
For you did it, you did it, you did it!
If you want to ride a bicycle and ride it straight and tall,
You can't simply sit and look at it 'cause it won't move at all.
But it's you who have to try it
And it's you who have to fall (sometimes)
If you want to ride a bicycle
And ride it straight and tall.
You've got to do it!

Every little bit, you've got to do it, do it, do it, do it.
And when you're through, you can know who did it
For you did it, you did it, you did it!
If you want to read a reading book
    and read the real words, too

You can't simply sit and ask the words
    to read themselves to you.
But you have to ask a person who can show you one or two
If you want to read a reading book
    and read the real words, too.
You've got to do it!

Every little bit, you've got to do it, do it, do it, do it.
And when you're through, you can know who did it
For you did it, you did it, you did it!
It's not easy to keep trying, but it's one good way to grow.
It's not easy to keep learning, but I know that this is so:
When you've tried and learned
You're bigger than you were a day ago.
It's not easy to keep trying, but it's one way to grow.
You've got to do it!

Every little bit, you've got to do it, do it, do it, do it.
And when you're through, you can know who did it,
For you did it, you did it, you did it!

You're the Only One

You're the only one who knows what you're thinking.
You're the only one.
You're the only one who knows how you're feeling.
You're the only one.

But if you'd like to share with another
That's for only you to do.
Since the only one who knows what you're thinking

Is you.

It's the People You Like the Most

It's the people you like the most
Who can make you feel maddest.

It's the people you care for the most
Who manage to make you feel baddest.

It's the people you like the most
Who can make you feel happiest!

It's the people you care for the most, most likely
Who manage to make you feel snappiest!

Love Is People

Love is people
Love is people needing people
Love is people caring for people
That is love.

Love's a little child
Sharing with another.
Love's a brave man
Daring to liberate his brother.

Love is people
Love is people needing people
Love is people caring for people
That is love.

And though some have costly treasure
It never seems to measure up
To people needing people
Caring for people
For that's love.

Love is people
People love.

You're Special

You're an ice cream cone
You're a lollipop
You're a baby chick
You're a pogo stick
You're a magic trick
You're a spinning top
You're special!

If someone asked me to relate
One reason you're so shiny
I'd really have to speculate
With eeny, meeny, miny.
You're a dancing doll
You're a shooting star
You're the foamy sea
You're a honeybee
You're a Christmas tree
You're a steel guitar
You're special!

You're a cowboy's horse
You're a baseball bat
You're a bright blue sky
You're a fishing fly
You're an apple pie
You're a pussy cat
You're special!

If someone asked me to confide
One reason you're so shiny
The only way I could decide
Is eeny, meeny, miny.
You're a swimming pool
You're a lightning bug
You're a smash homerun
You're a raisin bun
You're the noon day sun
You're a big bear hug
You're special!

Find a Star

Find a star, a star that seems just right
Wish with all your might, and then again
Find a star, don't let it out of sight
Wish with all your might again, and then . . .

Then find a wishbone
And find a four-leaf clover
And when the rain is over, find a rainbow
Go find a horseshoe
Go find a lucky penny
Just keep on wishing anyway.

Find a star, the same one every night
One that's shining bright and new for you
Find a star and cross your fingers tight
Then your wishes might come true.

Then find a wishbone
And find a four-leaf clover
And when the rain is over, find a rainbow
Go find a horseshoe
Go find a lucky penny
Just keep on wishing anyway.

Lyrics by Josie Carey, Music by Fred Rogers

A Smile's the Style

If you'd like to be in style
Here's a tip that's worth your while:
If you're happy, you'll look snappy
Just pick out your biggest smile.

No one really is impressed
With the way that we are dressed.
All the grinners are the winners
With a smile you'll look your best.

My suggestion is expression
Keep a bright look, it's the right look.
If your eyes glow and your teeth show
It's a sure sign that you feel fine.

You'll be welcome every place
And you'll win the fashion race.
If you're wearing and you're sharing
A real smile upon your face!

Lyrics by Josie Carey, Music by Fred Rogers

This Is Just the Day

If you've got an hour
Now's the time to share it.
If you've got a flower, wear it.
This is just the day.

If you've got a plan
Now's the time to try it.
If you've got an airplane, fly it.
This is just the day.

It's the day for seeing
All there is to see.
It's a day for being
Just you, just me.

If you've got a smile
Now's the time to show it.
If you've got a horn, then blow it.
It's the minute to begin it—
This is just the day.

Perfect Day

This day has really been unique
The wind and trees played hide-and-seek
The sun and clouds danced cheek-to-cheek
It's been a perfect day!

This day has really been so good
The sunshine shone just where it should
We all feel fine, let's knock on wood
It's been a perfect day!

Just ask the trees
Sheer perfection!
Ask the breeze
No objection!
Ask the bees
Near confection!
Sheer perfection, no objection, near confection, wow!

This day has really been the best
It certainly passed every test
From north to south and east to west
It's been a perfect day!

It's been a good day for a flower
It's been a good day for a tree
It's been a good day for a mushroom
    or a toadstool
It's been a good day for me.

This day has really been quite nice
The temperature took our advice
If you don't mind, we'll say it twice:
It's been a positively, absolutely perfect day!

I'm Proud of You

I'm proud of you
I'm proud of you
I hope that you're as proud as I am
Proud of you.
I'm proud of you
I hope that you are proud.

And that you're learning how important you are
How important each person you see can be
Discovering each one's specialty
Is the most important learning.

I'm proud of you
I'm proud of you
I hope that you're as proud as I am
Proud of you.
I'm proud of you
And I hope that you are proud of you, too!

Tomorrow

Tomorrow, tomorrow, we'll start the day
Tomorrow with a song or two.
Tomorrow, tomorrow, we'll start the day
Tomorrow with a smile for you.
I know tomorrow will be happy
And so tomorrow, make it snappy.
Tomorrow, tomorrow, it soon will be
Tomorrow and be our day, we'll say
A happy tomorrow to you!

It's Such a Good Feeling

It's such a good feeling
To know you're alive.
It's such a happy feeling
You're growing inside.
And when you wake up ready to say,
"I think I'll make a snappy new day!"
It's such a good feeling,
A very good feeling,
The feeling you know
You're alive!

It's such a good feeling
To know you're in tune.
It's such a happy feeling
To find you're in bloom.
And when you wake up ready to say,
"I think I'll make a snappy new day!"
It's such a good feeling
A very good feeling
The feeling you know
That we're friends.

Index of Song Titles

Index

𝓕red McFeely Rogers was born on March 20, 1928, in Latrobe, Pennsylvania. Rogers earned his bachelor's degree in music composition from Rollins College in Winter Park, Florida, in 1951. Upon graduation, he was hired by NBC as an assistant producer for *The Voice* of *Firestone* and, later, as floor director for *The Lucky Strike Hit Parade*, *The Kate Smith Hour*, and the *NBC Opera Theatre*. In 1952, Rogers married Joanne Byrd, a concert pianist and Rollins graduate.

In November 1953, at the request of WQED Pittsburgh, the nation's first community-sponsored educational television station,

Rogers produced *The Children's Corner*, a daily live hour-long visit with music and puppets. Rogers served as puppeteer, composer, and organist. In 1955, the show won the Sylvania Award for the best locally produced children's program in the country. It was on *The Children's Corner* that several regulars of *Mister Rogers' Neighborhood* made their debuts: Daniel Striped Tiger, X the Owl, King Friday XIII, Henrietta Pussycat, and Lady Elaine Fairchilde.

During his free time, Rogers attended the Pittsburgh Theological Seminary and the University of Pittsburgh's Graduate School of Child Development. He graduated from the seminary and was ordained a Presbyterian minister in 1963, charged with continuing his work with children and families through mass media. Later that year, Rogers was invited to create a program for the CBC in Canada that was called *Misterogers*. It was there that Fred Rogers made his on-camera debut as host.

When Rogers returned to Pittsburgh in 1966 with his family,

he incorporated segments of the CBC into a new series, which was distributed by the Eastern Educational Network. This series eventually became *Mister Rogers' Neighborhood*. In 1968 the program was made available for national distribution through the National Educational Television network (NET), which later became the Public Broadcasting Service (PBS).

Fred Rogers was the composer and lyricist of over two hundred songs, the author of numerous books for children, such as the First Experience series and the Let's Talk about It series, and the author of many books for adults, including *Mister Rogers Playtime Book*, *You Are Special*, *The Giving Box*, *Mister Rogers Talks with Parents*, and *Dear Mister Rogers: Does It Ever Rain in Your Neighborhood?*

Rogers received more than forty honorary degrees from distinguished educational institutions, among them Yale University, Carnegie Mellon University, Boston University, and his alma mater, Rollins College. He was awarded every major prize in television that he was eligible for, as well as many others from special-interest groups in education, communications, and early childhood development. In 1999 he was inducted into the Television Hall of Fame, and in 2002 President George W. Bush presented him with the Presidential Medal of Freedom, the nation's highest civilian honor. Rogers was recognized for his contribution to the well-being of children and for his career in public television that demonstrates the importance of kindness, compassion, and learning. "Fred Rogers has proven that television can soothe the soul and nurture the spirit and teach the very young," President Bush said.

Fred Rogers passed away on February 27, 2003, at his home in Pittsburgh, Pennsylvania. He is survived by his wife, Joanne Rogers, their two sons, and three grandsons.

Library of Congress Cataloging in Publication Number: 2018943034
Full CIP available on request.
ISBN: 978-1-68369-317-8
Printed in Canada
Typeset in Bookmania

Note: The songs on pages 17, 20, 28, 38, 44, 93, 112, 115, 128,
and 130 first appeared in *The Children's Corner*, hosted by Josie Carey
with puppets by Fred Rogers. These lyrics were written by Josie Carey,
to music by Fred Rogers.

Designed by Andie Reid and Doogie Horner
Illustrations by Luke Flowers
Editorial assistance by Rebecca Gyllenhaal
Production management by John J. McGurk

Quirk Books
215 Church Street
Philadelphia, PA 19106
quirkbooks.com
10 9 8 7 6 5 4 3 2 1

Opposite page: Fittingly, this book ends with an illustration of
Mr. Rogers on page 143. Fred Rogers considered the number 143
to be very special. He once said, "It takes one letter to say 'I' and
four letters to say 'love' and three letters to say 'you.' One hundred
and forty-three." He liked the number so much that he maintained
a weight of 143 pounds for the last thirty years of his life.

To learn more about Fred Rogers and the
Mister Rogers' Neighborhood TV show, visit MisterRogers.org.

The Working Office

Geoffrey Salmon

Design Council

The Working Office

First edition published in the
United Kingdom 1979
Design Council Publications
28 Haymarket London SW1Y 4SU

Illustrations by Ken Baker MSIAD
of Baker Design Associates

Printed and bound in the
United Kingdom by Hazell Watson
& Viney Ltd Aylesbury Bucks
Photosetting by Vantage
Photosetting Co Ltd Southampton
and London

Distributed by
Heinemann Educational Books Ltd
48 Charles Street
London W1X 8AH

British Library CIP Data

Salmon, Geoffrey
    The Working Office
    1. Office management 2. Office layout
    3. Small business – Management
    I. Title   II. Design Council
    651'.32   HF5547

ISBN 0 85072 090 7

CONTENTS

INTRODUCTION

A great deal has been written and published over the past few years about working conditions in offices. For the most part this has dealt with large offices, mainly those in new buildings. Yet of the estimated 24 per cent of the working population of Britain who are office workers, the majority are employed in smaller units of up to only 30 or so people. They may be solicitors or estate agents, warehouse staff or ticket clerks, builders or public relations men, and each office will have its own special requirements. But regardless of these, the efficiency and well-being of the people who work in these smaller offices depend to a large extent on one common factor – their immediate, personal office environment. This environment is not an abstract concept, but a practical reality made up of such commonsense elements at the right amount of working space, balanced heating, ventilation and acoustics, convenient and safe technical installations, reliable and practical equipment, decent lavatories and rest spaces and so on.

Smaller offices use an incredibly wide variety of equipment and furniture and occupy all sorts of buildings. They represent a considerable market in the property, equipment and furniture fields – customers for whom countless sales representatives and agents eagerly do battle. And yet, in spite of the vast number of people involved, there is no comprehensive guide providing an overall approach to the design and selection of the essential elements. This book endeavours to fill that gap.

What kind of guidance is needed? Clearly, short of a weekly agony column in some appropriate magazine, it would be impossible to cover every kind of day-to-day problem facing the worker in the smaller office. What we can do, however, is to try to identify fundamental points that need to be watched, whether one is organising a new office space or overcoming the defects of an old one.

A basic question is whether to concentrate more upon the old than the new. At any one time, depending usually on economic circumstances, the balance of interest will alter. The recent emphasis on reviving the centres of towns and cities has led to more conversion and upgrading of older buildings. But at the same time, relaxation of planning controls on office space of up to $2787m^2$ ($30,000ft^2$) suggests that there will be a continuing pressure for newly built small to medium-sized offices. So to emphasise either new or old building at the expense of the other is hardly likely to reflect present user needs or accommodation potential.

The smaller the space, the greater emphasis should be placed upon its efficient use. There tends to be more specialisation of tasks in the larger office. In a smaller office each person must be prepared, if only on economic grounds, to tackle a range of tasks with, possibly, a variety of equipment. This induces valuable flexibility in both attitude and function, which has considerable effect on the planning and productivity of the office. A broad planning strategy is not enough; detailed equipment and furniture requirements can easily wreck even the best intentions. Pinboards, basins, teacups, coathooks, typewriters, radiators, telephones, chairs, tables, lighting, partitions and so on are all essential parts of the office and must fit together well and work properly.

However comprehensive the guide, success depends ultimately on good management and clear decision making. The number of decisions required when planning a better office environment is considerable. Most of these decisions are linked, and it is therefore often difficult to know where to start. To simplify the problem, the sequence of this book follows the various stages of planning and equipping an office. It starts by discussing overall space needs and standards, continues through the planning of individual spaces, their servicing, decoration and equipment, and concludes by considering the professional advice required and the legislation that must be observed in order to achieve all this in practice. There is no reason why sections should not be referred to separately or out of sequence, provided that the interaction between all aspects of the office environment is kept constantly in mind.

Success will not be measured ultimately simply in terms of the colour of the receptionist's desk or the managing director's filing system, but in the way the office functions overall. Balanced design management can help to create an efficient office organisation, and that, surely, is a worthwhile aim.

SECTION ONE: *defining the problem*

Scope of the problem

The first thing to decide upon is the scope of the problem. Is your office utterly inadequate in space, location and size, or is it perfect in size but generally badly lit, heated and down at heel? People have been known to embark upon ambitious plans for new offices when what was really needed was a sensible reassessment of their existing quarters. There are also those who soldier on regardless, not only of the Offices Act (which prescribes pretty minimal standards), but of the commonsense comforts of staff and fundamental hygiene, when they should be making an entirely fresh start.

Deciding upon the scope is therefore a difficult question full of pitfalls, personal preferences and prejudices. The closeness of the working group in most smaller offices means that everyone has a viewpoint and is eager (indeed, is rather anxious) to ensure that it is heard and incorporated.

Staff consultation

Strong, dictatorial managements may decide to be high-handed under these circumstances and to them this book will be of little use. But consultation with staff is not only valuable in terms of acquiring information, but absolutely vital for the acceptance of even modest proposals. Unless people are involved in matters affecting their own working environment they can unconsciously sabotage the best intentions. They also tend to remain unconvinced as to the benefits of any improvements thrust upon them.

The project co-ordinator

Day-to-day problems on such matters as lighting or heating levels are normally solved as part of commonsense routine management, but if the scope is larger – for instance, the refurbishing of an entire office or the setting up of a new office elsewhere – then a different approach is required. Someone must be acknowledged as being responsible for discussing proposals with all those concerned, for consulting with the professionals who may be engaged, such as agents, architects and solicitors, and generally for setting up guidelines for everyone to work within. He or she is, in fact, a project co-ordinator; rather a grand name but absolutely descriptive of the role required of the person who will hold together the diverse information concerning people, furniture, equipment and costs which, properly co-ordinated, will add up to a first-class working environment.

Decisions on guidelines

What will need to be discussed in order to determine these guidelines, and perhaps act as a brief for the professional consultants? The questions fall into two distinct stages, the first of which is discussed in this section of the book. The second and more detailed stage is discussed in Section Two. First of all, to define the problem generally, we must ask the following:

1 What is the total amount of space required purely for office use?
2 How much space is required for ancillary use, that is for meeting rooms, rest rooms, bulk storage, cleaners/catering space and so on?
3 What degree of flexibility, of expansion and privacy is required in the offices?
4 What levels of heating, lighting, power, ventilation and other servicing are required?
5 What kind of quality, atmosphere or image is it hoped to achieve?

The answers to these questions often seem obvious and barely worthy of further thought by each individual, although it will be surprising how diverse their views will appear when actually stated. This is because it is extremely difficult for people to discuss their personal work spaces in abstract terms, or to see themselves as part of a work process that affects the overall office arrangement and is affected by the building itself. Because of this it is not a good idea to sketch general layouts at too early a stage. Lines on paper mean different things to different people, and an objective analysis is far more likely to result from written material than from a drawing unless the drawing is literally a diagram, illustrating principles only. Even in this case, it is remarkable how often theoretical diagrams are remembered later as precise layouts when their original purpose has been forgotten.

Returning to the questions asked above: if we wish to determine the total amount of office space, a certain amount of crystal ball gazing and intelligent anticipation is required. It is not something that can be checked directly by a measuring tape, and it is certainly better to over-estimate than otherwise. In fact, a variation of Parkinson's law seems to apply to all new offices whereby the normal numbers of personnel, pieces of furniture and equipment for which maximum working space has been carefully calculated will expand by at least 25 per cent once that office space becomes operational.

What must be sought in the first instance, however, is an area for actually working in, to which can then be added suitable areas for circulation and other space for essential, but not necessarily 'working', activities, including the reception and entrance areas etc.

Personal working space

No hard and fast rules exist for determining the area that an average office worker requires, since this will depend on the type of work done by the individual. For example, the actual net area occupied by a clerical worker with desk and chair may be as little as 2.3m² (25ft²), but the total area used by the same person during his work may easily be two or three times this figure. At least the same amount of space again is required to turn a chair around to get in and out, to open drawers or cupboards at knee height, to reach the waste paper basket and, occasionally, to stretch legs. To this must be added all, or some, of the space nearby that is supplementary to the job: coat storage, filing cabinets and so on. And when this total has been arrived at, further space must be added on as an allowance for access to the immediate working area; normally this will be of the order of 10 to 15 per cent in an open office.

If this exercise is carried out for every type of job in the office, a series of individual working areas will be deduced. The table on page 11 lists the people and functions for which space is required in a typical small office. The table on page 10 shows how the net working area for each of these spaces is built up. Excepting very senior management, the range of areas required for various levels of staff tend to fall between 5.5 and 13m² (60 to 140ft²), giving an average of 9.5m² (100ft²) per person. The disposition of people and the effect of enclosing walls or screens will then determine the amount of general circulation space required. If there is a large proportion of enclosed offices with full-height partitions around them, the use of corridors will add a further 15 per cent or so to the total of the individual working areas. Where partitions can be avoided (and this depends not only on space standards, but also on acoustics, heating and ventilation, as will be seen later) then some overlap between general circulation areas and work space circulation areas will be possible, with consequent economies in space.

Work space versus circulation space

This possibility has sometimes been used irresponsibly (under the guise of trendy 'landscaping') to cram extra people into an office floor regardless of other important environmental factors. But although open planning has the merit of creating surplus space, which provides useful flexibility in work flow and circulation, it should not be lightly adopted as an economy measure. Productivity can decrease with the reduction of space standards, mainly as a result of the distraction brought about by nearby movement and noise. It is reasonable to expect that, the more concentrated the mental task, the fewer people there should be in a given area. So the advantage of open planning must be seen in terms of the opportunity it provides for an increase in available working space for each person, with all the benefits that this implies.

Enclosure of working space

A further matter of detail to be borne in mind at this stage is the degree of enclosure required by individuals or working groups. If, for instance, everybody in the office must have a separate, reasonably quiet office, this implies certain types of building or even structural arrangements. Under these circumstances modern buildings designed for exclusively open-planned use may require modifications that are nearly as expensive as might be expected of an older building. Some firms may require a measure of both enclosed and open office space and here it must be remembered that structural, heating and ventilation arrangements may be affected by this need. In short, the building and its planning arrangements can heavily influence the work method and operation. Unless the two are reconciled, one or the other will have to be modified, altered or distorted, and extra expense will result.

Ancillary space

It is necessary to add a further figure for spaces that are ancillary to the actual work space before the overall net usable floor area is known. These ancillary spaces are an essential part of the office function but their space requirements are not so readily analysed as those of other work places. The need for these spaces varies from office to office so that each case must be assessed separately. They will include:

A reception or waiting area or room.
Meeting or conference (sometimes dining) space.
Display, promotional or exhibition space.
Central (bulk) storage.
Cleaners and catering space.
Rest rooms.
Space for any special telephone equipment.
Space for special machinery (print machines etc).

These ancillary spaces do not normally include lavatories, because, for the purposes of determining net usable office area, these are regarded as utilities costed separately from office space. Lavatories come in the same category as staircases, lifts, ducts and so on. In leasehold accommodation, these utilities are normally charged as a service within the overall rent. If special facilities, such as executive lavatories or shower rooms, are required over and above normally expected provision, then of course these should be added.

Where special equipment is involved, ancillary spaces may require a greater area than at first thought adequate. For instance, a heavy but small security safe may need a space over which to distribute its weight larger than its own physical dimensions. Circulation space is also required between these spaces and the offices they serve.

Reasons for early space assessment

At this stage it may be asked why it is necessary to obtain accurate net usable floor area so early in the planning process. Surely a quicker way would be to find out what space is on the market and then check whether people and spaces can be fitted into it? This is very often done in fact, but the process inevitably wastes more time than it saves. Intelligent assessment at an early stage enables the estate agent and architect to be briefed (see Section Seven). If they do their jobs properly they should thereby be able to sort out a limited number of options for further detailed examination, all of which will be capable of accommodating the office. It is obviously a very great advantage to be able to quote the minimum net usable floor area required.

Environmental standards

Environmental servicing standards also need consideration, at least in principle, early on. 'Need we bother about that at this early stage?' is a typical reaction when levels of heating, lighting and ventilation are mentioned. It is *not* absolutely essential if the office is not particularly worried about the standards that an existing building will offer, but extending or modifying existing services is very expensive and some decision at the outset as to whether these conditions should be 'fair', 'good', 'better' or 'first class' may help to avoid the worst shocks later on. Some offices may need to be noise-free, which implies either air-conditioning and double glazing or a site in the country. Some staff may abhor fluorescent lighting; others mediocre ventilation. Levels required or available should be stated.

Degree of flexibility

Just as important, but not so obvious, is the need to consider the degree of flexibility required by the office. Few offices remain for ever at one particular staffing pattern or size. All businesses expand or contract with time, often as a result of economic factors beyond their control. Such variations can be catered for if careful thought is given to layout, furniture and servicing. Some businesses can control their growth and anticipate expansion, and if this is the case it is sensible to set out the parameters. This is clearly much simpler in the case of a new building on an open site than it is with limited floor space in a multi-occupied block or an older building.

Image

Finally, the question of 'image' – the kind of presentation the office wants to put forward – should be considered. It may be argued that this is a transitory and superficial matter compared with the allocations of working areas, services

OPEN OR ENCLOSED SPACE	IMMEDIATE WORKING AREA REQUIRED	SPACE FOR CIRCULATION AND VISITORS	SPACE FOR SPECIAL FURNITURE OR EQUIPMENT	NET FUNCTIONAL SPACE	ADD 15% OF NET FUNCTIONAL SPACE FOR GENERAL ACCESS	ADD 15% OF NET FUNCTIONAL SPACE WHERE APPROACHED FROM CORRIDOR	GROSS SPACE REQUIRED BY THE PARTICULAR FUNCTION	IMPERIAL EQUIVALENT OF GROSS SPACE REQUIRED	SPACE REFERENCE
E	9·50	7·90	6·30	23·70	3·56	3·56	30·82	332 ft²	1
E	6·30	6·00	5·60	17·90	2·69	2·69	23·28	250 ft²	2
E	"	"	"	"	"	"	"	"	3
E	6·75	6·65	—	13·40	2·01	2·01	17·42	187 ft²	4
O	8·75	2·25	—	11·00	1·65	—	12·65	136 ft²	5
O	5·25	1·50	—	6·75	1·01	—	7·76	83 ft²	6
O	"	"	—	"	"	—	"	"	7
O	"	"	—	"	"	—	"	"	8
O	3·90	1·70	—	5·60	0·84	—	6·44	69 ft²	9
O	"	"	—	"	"	—	"	"	10
E	6·20	5·50	—	11·70	1·76	1·76	15·22	163 ft²	11
E	"	"	—	"	"	"	"	"	12a
E	same person, but space added for future use						"	"	12b
O	2·80	1·40	—	4·20	0·63	—	4·83	52 ft²	13
O	"	"	—	"	"	—	"	"	14
E	4·50	4·75	1·00	10·25	1·54	1·54	13·33	143 ft²	15
O	2·30	—	—	2·30	0·35	—	2·65	29 ft²	16
O	"	—	—	"	"	—	"	"	17
E	16·75	—	1·50	18·25	2·74	2·74	23·73	255 ft²	18
E	7·50	—	—	7·50	1·13	1·13	9·76	105 ft²	19
O	this function to be part of Waiting Area						—	—	20
E	9·50	—	—	9·50	1·43	1·43	12·36	133 ft²	21

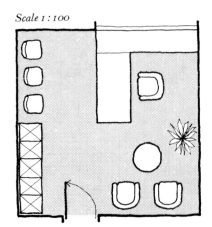

Scale 1 : 100

2 Finance Director

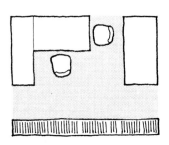

5 Senior Clerk

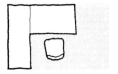

13 Audio Typist

 TOTAL: 263 m² (2829 ft²)

Work space analysis and office relationship diagram

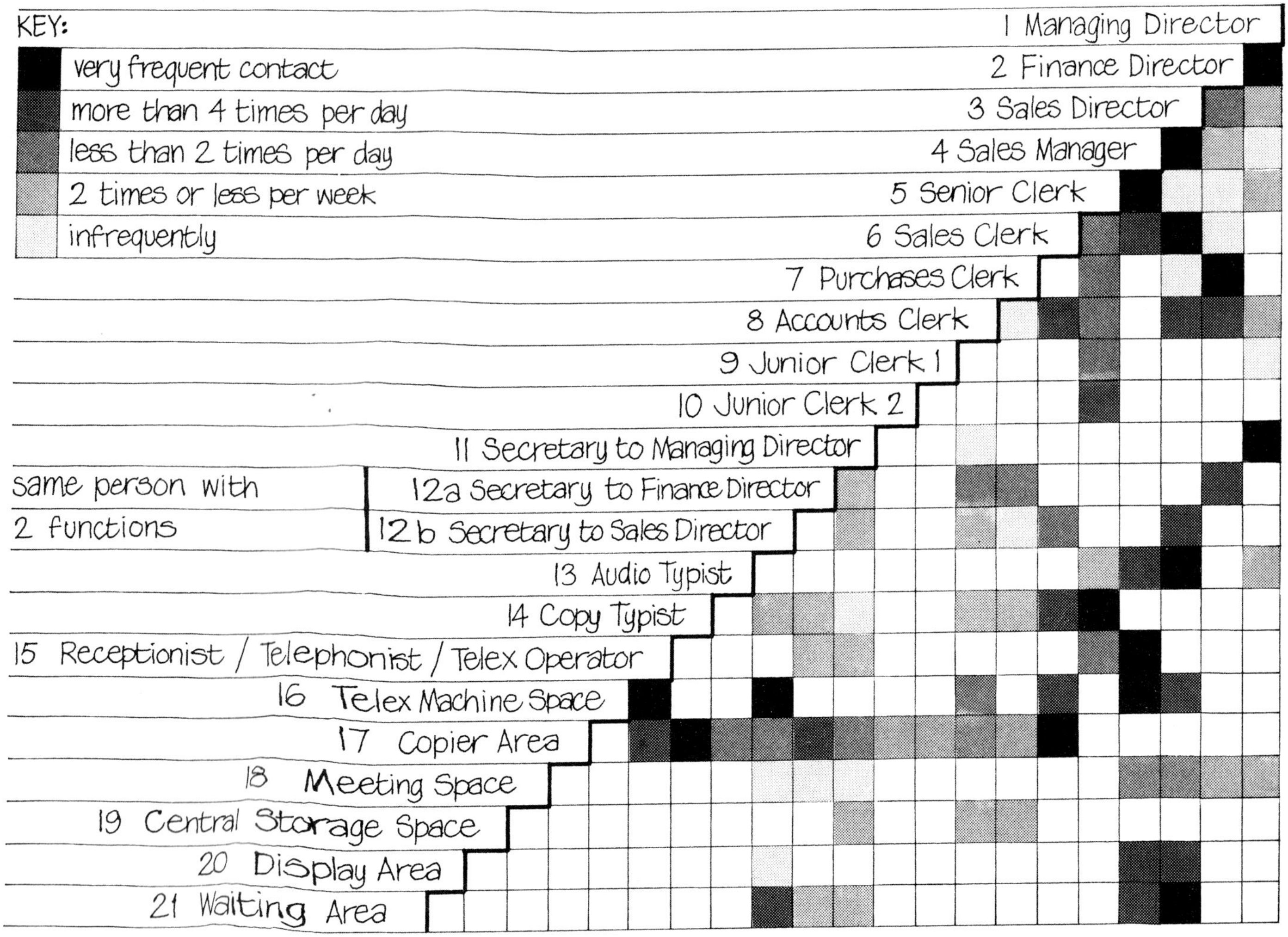

KEY:

■ very frequent contact	
■ more than 4 times per day	
■ less than 2 times per day	
■ 2 times or less per week	
■ infrequently	

1 Managing Director
2 Finance Director
3 Sales Director
4 Sales Manager
5 Senior Clerk
6 Sales Clerk
7 Purchases Clerk
8 Accounts Clerk
9 Junior Clerk 1
10 Junior Clerk 2
11 Secretary to Managing Director
12a Secretary to Finance Director
12b Secretary to Sales Director
13 Audio Typist
14 Copy Typist
15 Receptionist / Telephonist / Telex Operator
16 Telex Machine Space
17 Copier Area
18 Meeting Space
19 Central Storage Space
20 Display Area
21 Waiting Area

same person with
2 functions

and so on, but this quality lies at the back of most people's minds when they discuss their offices, and it can save endless time, both in searching for space and in detailed design, if this is recognised at the start. The image of a company grows naturally out of the efficiency and appearance of its work place and the behaviour of its employees, and in this sense it is far from superficial. It does not necessarily imply extra cost, moreover, since it is usually recognisable in the consistency and directness evident in all aspects of a company's design policy.

The next step
Once these guidelines have been assessed they should be discussed again with those who will be affected – preferably informally. Very often further ideas will emerge – some useless but others of value. Naturally it is managements' responsibility to decide which ideas can be adopted, but consultation, whether it is about a change in premises or in lighting levels, usually creates sympathy for the problem. It also makes sense of the comings and goings of architects, surveyors, builders, electrical engineers and so on whose presence might otherwise be viewed with apprehension.

As a result of the work described above it will be possible to make a start on a feasibility study by professionals. The object of this study will be to examine a limited number of propositions and make recommendations, which should essentially include an assessment as to cost and programme. These two elements – cost and programme – will enable the project co-ordinator to build up a capital budget for the proposal. Care must be taken that there are neither large gaps nor overlaps with budgetary information which may come from other sources: for instance from furniture and equipment suppliers. Care must also be taken to assess running costs; this is often neglected in the excitement of pursuing a new venture.

Checklist: *defining the problem*

1	2	3	4	5	6	7
What is the scope of the problem?	Has everyone whose workspace will be affected been consulted? Is a person available to act as project co-ordinator?	What amount of purely office working space is required? What proportion of private to open space is required? What amount of ancillary space is required? What degree of flexibility and expansion is required? What levels of environmental and technical servicing are required? What quality and image are sought?	What is the number of people in the office? What is the average net working area per person? What proportion has been added to the total net working area to allow for circulation between private offices? What degree of confidentiality is required in private offices? What gross areas have been allowed for: Reception/Waiting Meeting/Conference Display/Exhibition Central storage Cleaning/Catering Lavatories Rest rooms Telephone equipment Special equipment	Has a net useable office floor area been determined? Have professionals been appointed to look at existing premises? Have professionals been appointed to look at new premises? Have professionals been appointed to analyse space and/or equipment needs? Have professionals been appointed to analyse budgetary requirements?	Has a feasibility study produced a solution in terms of modifying existing offices? Has a feasibility study produced a solution in terms of moving to new offices? Has a feasibility study produced a solution in terms of capital costs of alternatives? Has a feasibility study produced a solution in terms of running costs of alternatives?	Has a clear decision to proceed or not to proceed been made as a result of the feasibility study?

SECTION TWO: *planning in detail*

The need for detailed definition

The next stage should examine the different spaces required in the offices in more detail. We need to define their positions and how they are linked together. In order to do this, careful thought must be given to three important matters:

1 How does work flow through the office?
2 How often do people move about the office?
3 Which people (or equipment) need private offices?

These questions may be fairly meaningless to a very small office which works in only one or two rooms. They are often more difficult for a larger office to answer because more activities and more spaces are usually involved, and because they rarely stop to ask themselves how their work gets done. But an architect/designer will need to be briefed on how the office works before beginning detailed planning. It is important therefore to examine this with care.

Relationship diagrams

One convenient way of finding out how people link up with others in the office is by means of a 'relationship diagram', as on page 11. This requires records to be kept over, say, a typical five-day week of the movement between rooms or people. It can be used for various purposes: for instance to find the frequency of paperwork or of internal telephone calls, and to express this visually. The information may seem to be self-evident, but sometimes such a diagram can illustrate in a simple and direct way that Miss Smith and Miss Brown have not the slightest need to sit near Mr Jones and that time is wasted if they do so. Whether they should be allowed to continue is clearly a subjective decision and not an operational one!

A diagram such as this will begin to indicate the best staff locations in a broad way. But before settling them, it is worth making distinctions between work characteristics or needs. This can be done by grouping 'noisy' versus 'quiet', 'confidential' versus 'non-confidential', or 'private' versus 'general' areas – whichever is the predominant consideration. The point of this is to get priorities established. If grouping is based on the relative needs of confidentiality, for instance, then the eventual layout will be confused if it is compromised by the insistence of some people that they should be near an external wall or entrance.

Enclosing walls and screens

These simple studies should begin to indicate the outlines of a general plan. An architect/designer will probably draw this as a series of 'balloon' shapes, as shown on the back cover of this book, rather than as a proper plan with rooms and walls. This is because at least one other important factor should be judged and settled before a real plan can be drawn up. This concerns the extent of enclosing walls and screens around spaces (which has already been referred to in Section One). Which spaces are to be partitioned off and which are to be entirely open? The work already done will almost certainly heavily influence this; walls and doors are very often a nuisance except where privacy or quiet are essential. When a lot of movement happens between work places they are often best omitted. Not surprisingly at this point some people insist on an enclosed space because of some special priority, normally 'confidentiality', that has not been mentioned before! The degree to which individuals are allowed to create private enclosures is a matter of some importance. Some people do find totally open office space uncomfortable, and they seem to work better when shut off by walls or screens from others. But even in open office spaces, individuals and groups are often divided up by filing cabinets and so on, which form fairly substantial boundaries. While in very large offices the layout does tend to be dictated primarily by work flow, in a smaller office other more persona factors must often be allowed to prevail.

Fire escape

A significant point that must be borne in mind at this stage is that of fire escape routes. This is very important because, in concentrating upon efficient planning at this early stage, fire escape needs are often overlooked or underestimated. As soon as the most elementary plan emerges from the studies outlined above, the local Fire Authority should be asked to comment and, if necessary, they may ask for modifications. Commonsense in planning fire escapes is a good guide, but it is not enough. Many factors are involved beyond the immediate problem of planning the office layout. Such matters as the age, location and construction of the building affect the outcome and expert advice is essential. Further discussion of fire escape requirements is included in Section Eight.

Space dispositions and the disabled

At this stage, therefore, a general disposition of spaces will have emerged that shows various functions, rooms and spaces in general terms – probably no more than a series of drawn rectangles marked 'Reception', 'Waiting', 'Meeting Room', 'Director's Office', 'Sales Group' and so on, joined by other rooms or corridors to one another and to entrances and exits. More detailed design thought is now required to tackle this in greater detail.

Before doing so, keep in mind the special needs of the disabled. The Department of Employment requires that all firms with a staff of 20 or more employ a quota of 3 per cent registered disabled people.

Their needs are not in fact very extraordinary, but they are too often entirely forgotten. Small, detailed considerations relating to handrails, door widths, changes in floor levels, a special lavatory and so on, can contribute enormously to making their disability less burdensome and their work more fulfilling.

Let us now consider each space in the office, what its detailed function is, and how its furniture and equipment might be planned.

Entrance and reception

The entrance area must fulfil three purposes: first, it must receive visitors; second, it should provide security or a vetting process to prevent unwanted visitors; and third, it should set the tone of the office in its appearance, atmosphere and efficiency. For a very small office the entrance may lead directly into the working area with the responsibility for receiving visitors resting on someone working there. Some boundary line should, however, be drawn, perhaps only a table, to prevent the visitor moving into the office before being vetted and welcomed. This notion of a boundary – a place for the visitor to pause, take stock and be welcomed – is a good one even for offices that wish to be so completely open as to allow the visitor to see the whole operation at work upon entering. In other offices, the reception area may well be linked with secretarial or typing space, with a desk or high counter as the boundary. Sometimes a separate entrance lobby will be divided from the reception by a wall or high screen with an opening or hatch through it. Such a full-height fire-resisting wall is sometimes

necessary for fire escape route reasons and, if so, a self-closing hatch will be insisted on by the authorities. Some typical arrangements for various kinds of entrance area are shown in the plans opposite.

Attention to detail is important in the reception area. Hard-headed businessmen may think that they are unsusceptible to colours, textures and modern prints, but even they will certainly notice tatty carpets, dirty walls or dingy lighting, and it is hard to avoid drawing conclusions about the firm's efficiency in consequence. For example, one vitally important detail is the firm's name-plate and any directional signs at the entrance leading to the reception. Entry to any office begins on the street, and signs should be explicit, easy to read and well designed. A letter-box of convenient size and a bell push are two other essentials that are often overlooked. Sometimes a small waiting-room, which can double as an interview room, placed next to the entrance is valuable. But at the very least, one or two comfortable chairs, perhaps a table, and a relaxed, pleasant atmosphere are to be expected. Is there a convenient cupboard or stand for dripping overcoats and umbrellas? Is a telephone close at hand? These are minimum courtesies. A demonstration of forethought and care can be psychologically important to visitors and help to set the right tone for efficent business.

Attention to detail in the reception area must also extend to security. Vetting a visitor can be done tactfully in person by a full-time receptionist, but this can be

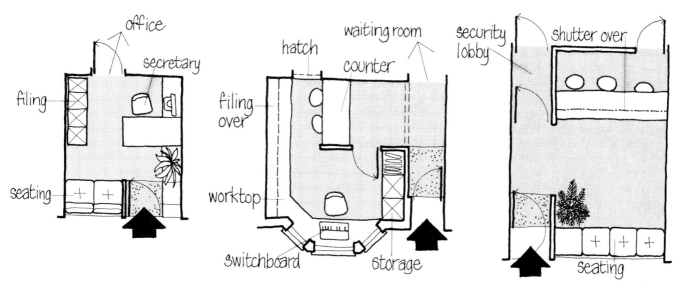

office

secretary

filing

seating

hatch

waiting room

counter

filing over

worktop

switchboard

storage

security lobby

shutter over

seating

ABOVE *Entrance layout varies with function, and the boundary line for visitors changes accordingly. The left hand plan shows a layout for a small professional firm; the centre for a group medical practice; and the right for the entrance and pay-in desk of a building society branch. (Plans scale 1:100)*

BELOW *An intelligent use of space combined with simple, hard-wearing materials give freshness and interest to this small entrance area serving offices in a converted London warehouse. The view through the enquiry hatch shows a busy working office: time is unlikely to be wasted here.*

TOP LEFT AND RIGHT *Modular upholstered seating units such as these can provide a relaxed waiting area of any suitable size, and in almost any enclosed or open space. Those on the right are best suited to restricted rectangular spaces; those on the left snake along to occupy any available area.*

BELOW LEFT *Crisp design with clear definition of space and function make this reception area an attractive place to enter or to sit or work in. It helps to reinforce the image of its occupants, who provide office cleaning services.*

BELOW *In spite of the demands of the existing structure, space appears to flow effortlessly in this office in a converted brickmaking factory in the Midlands. Indeed, the contrast between rough brickwork, textured baffled ceiling, hair carpet tiles and white laminate covered furniture seems to endow these spaces with a greater lightness than many much larger open-plan offices achieve.*

expensive. If the front door is kept closed and locked, as it is in many smaller professional offices, a door-opening mechanism with a phone link between the door and an internal desk can be the solution. Further door security can be applied in special cases – for example, between a reception area and an office handling large sums of money or valuable objects. Two-door lobbies, with one door operated from each side and with small glass inspection panels, may be used in this case.

Open offices

The term 'open office' is normally applied to any large office space in which staff of various levels of responsibility work together without dividing walls. In this sense, it is an updated description of the old 'general office' but with a better understanding as to the environmental quality provided. In the pre-Office Act era, the general office was an often neglected space where a ruthless manoeuvring for work positions adjacent to radiators, light switches or windows damaged productivity.

Open-plan offices are now almost universally visualised as being pleasant, evenly lit, warmed and ventilated spaces suitable for occuption by all levels of staff. It is, in fact, difficult to attract staff if the environment is otherwise. The amount of space to be allowed in planning will vary considerably. First of all it depends upon needs of the different jobs carried on within it: typical sizes for various job levels are shown on page 10. But the overall area calculated from these may very well require to be increased to allow for additional flexibility, confidentiality, or the possibility of staff expansion. This is especially true where the entire office is open-plan with everyone, including executives, in one work space. The density of occupation must vary accordingly: those with more confidential or quiet work will necessarily have claim to more space per head. If the average working area per person of 9.5m² suggested on page 8 is adopted, variations on this will be possible to meet individual requirements and still maintain reasonable space standards. Thus, for an open office holding 15 people, the area allocated – which includes space for furniture and equipment – will be in the region of 15 times 9.5m² or 143m² (1500ft²).

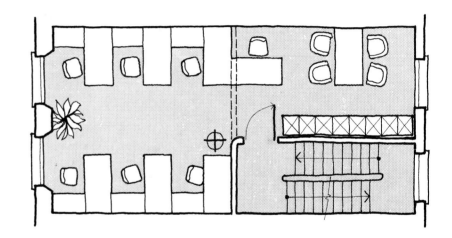

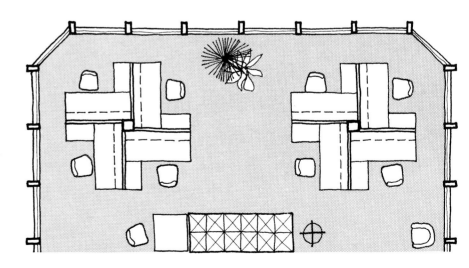

The arrangement of work space is usually dictated by the building plan. The top layout is that necessarily adopted on an eighteenth-century terrace house first floor; the other shows the less constrained arrangement possible in part of one floor of a modern building. Nevertheless, the former may suit its own particular office operation just as well as the latter. (Plans scale 1:100)

An examination of the way in which work is handled will quickly show where people should sit in order to carry out their tasks, move easily to filing, storage and equipment, or circulate through the office. Well designed heating and lighting installations are, of course, essential in this space.

Many offices are limited in width or length, but as a general rule, the best use of any space will be to have a simple layout with desks parallel with, or at a constant angle to the perimeter. This may not look very exciting, but most office furniture will then fit in conveniently without wasting space. Illustrations of 'landscaped' offices may suggest that by placing desks at a variety of angles to one another, all sorts of layout problems will be magically solved. But properly 'landscaped' offices are the result of rigid operational layout criteria applied to staff numbers normally in excess of 50 and in very controlled environments. Attempts to imitate such layouts, visually, in smaller offices, may result in considerably more wasted space than if a very simple, straightforward layout had been adopted.

Smaller open-plan offices can often look more attractive and more personable than the large landscaped office. Furniture and

screening affect the sense of space considerably, and must be positioned with care. Many of the most recent office screening systems tend to define individual territories by creating small cells with walls which can only just be looked over. If these are clumsily planned, a series of enclosed, virtually private, spaces are created. These can offset the main advantage of the open plan: that is the simplification of work flow. Numerous screens of even medium height often interfere with heat distribution and sometimes

with lighting. It is true that flexible screening does have advantages for offices that have a real need for heavily screened, separate work spaces, especially in rented open office space, and where full height partitions are not suitable. Other advantages of screening systems are, of course, that they can support pin-up boards, shelving and desk tops as part of a co-ordinated design.

The positions and availability of telephones and power outlets are especially important in an open office. Where the width of an office

exceeds about 6m, telephone and electricity cables cannot be stretched from the perimeter walls without the hazard of people tripping over them. Special floor or ceiling ducting may be necessary to carry them to desks in the centre of the office. Open offices should never be planned as wholly internal spaces, ringed by private offices which alone have the benefit of window views. This arrangement usually creates problems of ventilation and is thoroughly bad psychologically. Everyone in an open office should be able to look up from work and see a distant window and, if possible, a view – however limited.

Where several people work together at different tasks and often with different equipment in an open office, even slight interruptions increase in significance. A loud voice, the chatter of a typewriter or telex, a flickering fluorescent tube, a cold draught – all these seem more noticeable and disruptive. These environmental factors must be capable of control. Good planning, good acoustics, regularly maintained lighting, efficient heating and ventilation and so on, are essential if the open plan is to work. It is better to avoid an open office altogether if there is going to be doubt about this, for otherwise it may prove to be more trouble than it is worth.

Private and enclosed offices

Private offices are, at least in theory, occupied by people who either have especially confidential business or who will be unduly distracted by noise, movement, or other disturbances elsewhere in the office. Apart from this, it is undeniably

rather enjoyable to have a personal office, a kind of home from home where one is not overlooked. The smallest enclosed office which is tolerable for one person to work in, without visitors, should never be less than 5.5m² (60ft²), assuming a ceiling height not less than 2.4m. The Offices Act permits a minimum of 3.7m² (40ft²) per person – or 11.33m³ (400ft³) – but this is inadequate and deserves revision. The minimum width of a private office should never be less than 1.8m which, working on the minimum area of 5.5m², will give a length of about 3m.

These dimensions produce a narrow, deep room which will only accommodate a 1500×750mm desk placed parallel to the longest wall, two 700×450mm filing cabinets and one chair. The parts of the floor area that remain will probably be taken up by a waste paper basket and perhaps a heater. Changing the proportions will help, but enough has been said to show that the provision of small enclosed rooms is not necessarily a good investment. They can positively hinder work flow and information exchange and reduce efficiency.

Sometimes it is convenient for junior staff to work in an enclosed room rather than in a larger office with others. This may be the case with a copy typist who would otherwise distract the office or a layout draughtsman who has need of special equipment or layout space. A 5.5m² area room may then very well satisfy such needs. For more senior staff and executives the following *minimum* areas per head are given as a guide to the size of their private offices. These can be increased to

cover special circumstances.

Senior Clerk, secretary or bookeeper	9m²
Manager or professional	14m²
Director, senior management and professionals	20m²

All these floor areas assume ceiling heights not less than 2.4m. Note that these are considerably less than those assumed for the tables on pages 10 and 11.

Very often enclosed offices are sized and laid out without regard for the furniture to be put in them. If a general idea of the shapes and sizes of furniture and equipment can be determined at an early stage, it will do a great deal to help efficient planning. Whatever the status of the occupant, he or she will usually impose their character on private work space, if only in minor unconscious ways. This is well and good if everyone starts off on an equal footing. But an agreed provision on the quantity and standards of things such as pinboard, storage, and telephones should be settled at the outset for everyone if petty jealousies are to be avoided.

Secretarial space

The range of tasks carried out by a secretary is a very wide one and,

Secretarial space must cater for a wide range of functions of which typing is only a small part. Unless a generous working area is available the space will become cluttered, papers mislaid and expensive time wasted. If possible, equipment and references should be mounted on adjoining walls or screens to keep the desk clear. A large pin-up board and about one metre of shelf space are essential. Note that the smaller typing desk is 50mm lower than the main work surface. (Plan scale 1:100)

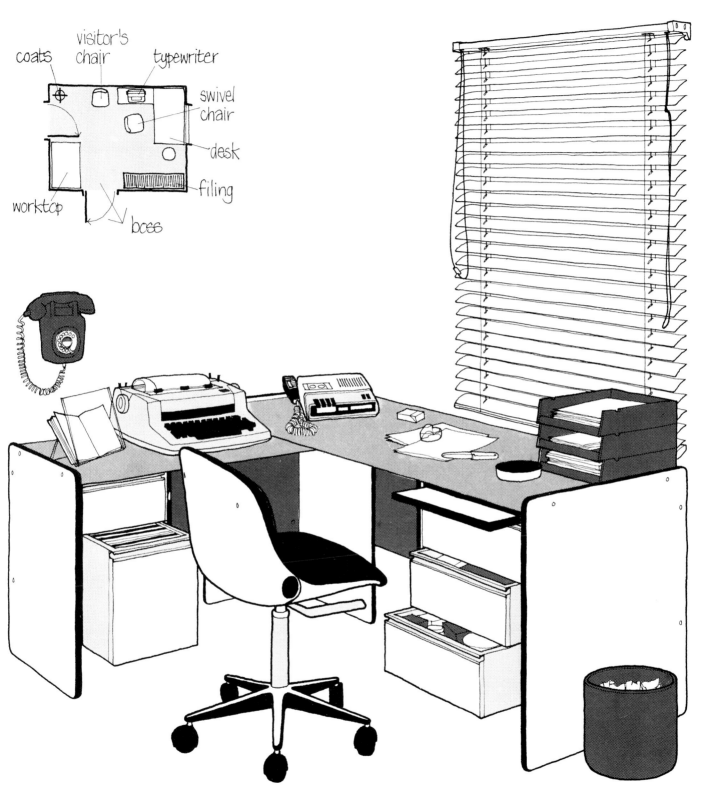

coats
visitor's chair
typewriter
swivel chair
desk
filing
worktop
boss

unfortunately, is not always fully appreciated. These tasks usually comprise the transcription of documents by typing or other means, filing, frequent use of the telephone, visiting and passing messages to other people, co-ordinating and arranging administrative matters, purchasing stocks, and so on. Some secretaries have an even wider range of work, but this list serves to emphasise how important are the space, furniture and equipment required.

For this, the typewriter is the key piece of equipment, but unless the secretary is in effect only a typist, (who has an entirely different and more limited function) a typewriter is only part of the equipment. The secretary will also need a large desk or table area, as uncluttered as possible by telephones or other equipment so that collating, comparing, filing and sorting can be carried out at any time undisturbed. There should also be adequate storage space for immediate supplies of stationery and for personal belongings. Easily accessible shelving and generous pinboard space are needed in the near vicinity, although it is difficult to generalise on dimensions. One metre length of shelving is the least to contemplate for a set of telephone directories and reference books and this may be inadequate for some offices where a wide range of references is essential – for instance in publishing. It is also better to provide extra pin-up space rather than suffer the decorative ravages of the drawing pin on normal wall surfaces.

The typewriter desk, together with space for all the paraphernalia associated with typing, should

therefore be a virtually separate piece of furniture specially designed for that particular function. Ideally the typewriter should be at a level about 50mm *lower* than surrounding desk height, and there should be ample space for reference documents on either side. Very often secretaries are given enough worktop area and equipment, but inadequate room to move about easily and quickly to carry out their many tasks. Space must be left to enable movement around their desk when doors and drawers are open.

The telephone in particular must be positioned with care and it may be worth considering the use of a loudspeaker type or amplifier rather than a normal handset in order to save space and allow free movement while using it.

Last but not least is the secretary's chair. Many comfortable chairs are available, but more than just comfort is at stake. The chair must be fully adjustable, easily moved (although some secretaries abhor castors) and capable of swivelling. Arms to the chair can be a nuisance, comfortable though they may be for tasks other than typing. More is said about types and dimensions of furniture in Section Five.

Executive offices

Executive space usually reflects executive style. The planning problems are often as much psychological as they are functional. For instance, some executives may really prefer a discursive, creative atmosphere in their office, yet adopt seating arrangements which symbolise autocratic attitudes. Others reverse the order, much to the confusion of everyone.

Possibly the one common factor in executives' work is the way it varies in intensity and type week by week. This means that they must have books, paper, equipment and storage immediately available to cater for all their purposes. The archetypal leather-topped desk is not necessarily the best piece of furniture to choose, well established though it may be as a status symbol. Once again, it is a good idea to list the activities which will take place in the executive office and the space, furniture and equipment required. These activities may include formal meetings with a number of outside visitors, more casual meetings with office colleagues, telephone calls both internal and external, reading letters or documents, referring to books or files and comparing reports. This list will indicate the range of movement, and the worktop, shelf space and seating required in the room. A large conventional desk may not always be the best answer; a small desk and a couple of small tables may be ideal. A wide range of furniture exists which can usually suit all requirements, including seating and storage; the latter in particular deserves more attention in executive offices than it normally gets.

In theory, we often hear that the really efficient executive needs a very

This Production Manager's office in a small components company reflects a no-nonsense, slightly austere concern for the business in hand. Generous pin-board space and an adaptable work surface are useful features. Visitors' chairs are adequately comfortable, but not so much as to delay departure. The manager's chair is a straightforward modern design and underlines the overall sense of efficiency. (Plan scale 1:100)

telephone/
dictaphone, etc.

pinboard

coats

swivel
chair

stacked
chairs

extension
desk

filing

1979 J F M A M J J A S O N D

23

small work surface. But in many businesses to which the theorists never penetrate, there is a need for table space simply to put down and pick up quickly a variety of papers at different times throughout each working day. Einstein adopted this approach in his study and is reputed to have described the result as 'meaningful clutter'.

Other executive offices act more as public relations salons. Suitably furnished and decorated, they extend the purpose and personality of the business and its proprietors.

The executive office will in any case tend to reflect the function of its occupant: a sales manager may need a display of photographs of company products, with suitable lighting; a production manager will need well lit space for wall charts and lots of seating, with efficient ventilation; those in an advising or negotiating role should sensibly pay more than usual attention to the number and comfort of visitors chairs.

The telephone is a key instrument to the executive. Telephones must be easily accessible and there is

certainly an advantage in using the loudspeaker type or other means of amplification to allow examination of documents while telephoning. Where large numbers of personal files or records must be within immediate reach, special filing units are available to stand near the executive's desk (see Section Six).

The position of the executive's desk relative to a window is sufficiently important to deserve special mention. In many cases he choses to sit behind the desk with his back to the window. This forces a visitor facing the desk to blink into strong contrasting light and obscures the executive's features, reducing effective communication. The moral is clear.

Mention must also be made of the Victorian idea of a 'partners room' which is shared by several executives. This has recently returned to favour since more generous individual standards can be achieved in this way where overall space is limited. If the design is carried out carefully, more facilities can be provided at a lower cost than with separate offices.

Meeting rooms

An imaginitively designed meeting room can extend the potential of an office immeasurably. In addition to conferences, it can be used for entertainment and dining, film, video or other presentation, interviewing and for internal office

This meeting table is built up from separate units, each of which can be used by itself. The arrangement means that a meeting room can be easily adapted for other purposes.

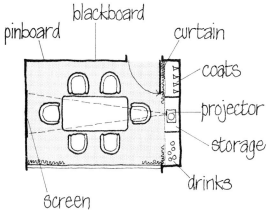

pinboard blackboard curtain coats projector storage drinks screen

A small meeting room can provide all the basic essentials in a relatively simple way without wasting space. Storage, drinks and so are hidden behind a curtain and a projection screen is fixed permanently to one wall. Ventilation is particularly important, especially if the window has to be obscured during slide projection. (Plan scale 1 : 100)

seminars. Special importance attaches to the meeting room where an office contains a large proportion of open-planning, and it must be located accordingly. Frequent meetings with visitors from outside the office will suggest a position close to the entrance, preferably adjoining Reception. Elsewhere it must be accessible from a passageway of generous width. It may, alternatively, be an extension of an executive office from which it may be divided using sliding folding doors.

The planning of a meeting room is primarily dependent upon the size and shape of the meeting table, which will almost certainly be the largest piece of furniture in the room. The style of meeting characteristic of the office is important here because it affects the actual shape of the table. If very formal meetings with a chairman are held, then a rectangular table is most appropriate, its length dependent on numbers. More than 10 people around a table would suggest a slightly shaped table top which is wider at its middle than at its ends.

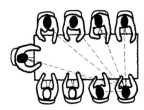

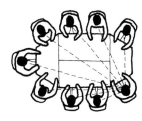

This allows everyone to see and hear with ease.

Other shapes of table, for instance circular or horseshoe-shaped ones, may better suit other kinds of meeting. Circular tables are often useful for 'think tank' sessions; other shapes can be built up if the table is made up in separate sections which are capable of being joined in a number of different ways. Tables should be generous in their width, regardless of their shape, so as to allow ample space for documents, cups, ashtrays and perhaps sandwich plates. If people are to sit on both sides of the tables, then a width less than 900mm is impractical.

Chairs around the meeting table should be comfortable, firm and capacious enough to avoid that rather unpleasant tiredness which comes from prolonged sitting with limited space for movement. More than the average width is therefore required and where they have castors a minimum space of 700mm should be allowed per chair to allow easy access. When not on castors, chairs should be of reasonable weight for easy movement – however capacious they may be; manufacturers do not always recognise this. Armchairs are relaxing providing that they are not so high as to prevent the chair being pulled up to the table, nor so low as to send the occupant to sleep.

Generally too little space is allowed in the meeting room for this essential furniture – quite apart from other functions the room may serve. For a rectangular table, the room must allow about 1.5m^2 (16ft^2) per head for 10 or more people. Below this number more space should be

allowed per head as appropriate.

There is almost always a need for wall charts, blackboards, projection screens or television in the meeting room and the presentation of materials, merchandise or designs may be involved. Such equipment must be capable of being handled easily without too much disturbance of papers or furniture. Presentation is best done on a separate table or wall shelves away from, but visible to, the meeting table. The ceiling can incorporate a projection screen and support a projector operated by remote control. Wall surfaces can be designed to accept charts pinned directly to them. Wall display systems are sometimes a useful permanent fixture for sales or presentation purposes. Also vertically hinged wall screens can display large numbers of charts and so on while taking up very little space. For advertising and design agencies, a small projection room is a relatively simple yet impressive arrangement, which will also act as a film or slide store.

Sometimes the meeting room doubles up as a dining and hospitality room. This idea is increasingly popular where space for a small, highly efficient (and certainly well ventilated) kitchen is available immediately adjoining. Storage of cutlery, table and glassware is then required together with drinks storage. These can be in a built-in-cupboard or furniture cabinet in the meeting room. Where space is in short supply, the former is preferable.

It is worth emphasising that prolonged meetings can be physically and emotionally exhausting, so heating, ventilation, lighting and acoustics, as well as furniture, must be designed with care. Dimmer controls for lighting are a good idea, especially when film projection is contemplated. If meetings are frequent, or alternate with dining, consideration should be given to installation of an air-conditioning unit or mechanical ventilation. Meeting rooms that reverberate, have glaring lights and hard, uncomfortable chairs, or are hot and stuffy, positively slow up business, yet it is astounding how many offices tolerate them.

Lavatories and rest rooms

The British tend to be puritanical about lavatories, and many smaller firms put up with the most basic, utilitarian facilities. Most staff today, however, expect rather better than minimal standards. One of the problems, of course, is that smaller firms frequently occupy buildings that are 50 years old or more, with ancient plumbing and drainage systems that are difficult and expensive to modify. Such buildings were also rarely planned so that lavatories could be altered or

extended easily. The price per square metre for converting or upgrading lavatories is sometimes as high as for an executive office or meeting room in the same office, and this may be difficult to justify when costs have to be pruned to meet budgets. Too often the lavatory accommodation suffers as a result, which is a mistake because it pays to be ahead of the field. What is barely acceptable today usually looks fairly old fashioned in a few years.

Space standards allowed (and usually recommended) in lavatories are generally far too low and tend to ignore the peak periods of use, which are just before people leave at midday or in the evening.

The following guide should therefore be followed wherever possible:

Both sexes

WCs	*Hand basins*
1 for 1–10	1 for 1– 5
2 for 11–20	2 for 5–15
3 for 20–30	3 for 15–30

For men
Urinals
1 for 1–10
2 for 11–20
3 for 20–30

Provision should also be made for disabled people. For ambulant disabled persons, at least one WC

This room is designed to enable a firm of industrial designers to make presentations of filmed, graphic and packaging material in a small space. All lighting is adjustable in position and brightness. Display items can be hung or bracketed from timber wall or ceiling slats. A film projection room is concealed behind the pinboard panels, with an aperture between them on the left of the picture. The opposite wall has a permanent white screen.

Conversion of older property to office use generally involves upgrading the existing lavatories. Illustrated here is a typical before and after case, for use by men. A women's lavatory could be provided in a similar way, with a separate cleaner's cupboard situated elsewhere.

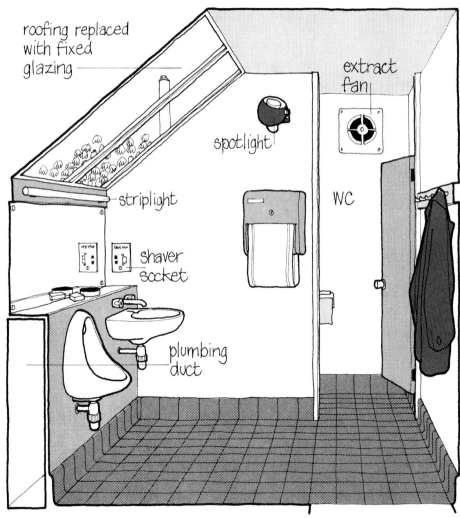

roofing replaced with fixed glazing

extract fan

spotlight

striplight

WC

shaver socket

plumbing duct

compartment should be 800mm in width, at least 1700mm deep if the door opens inwards (1500 if it opens outwards) and with a 30mm diameter support rail on either side. It is well worth providing a WC that can cater for wheelchair users. The minimum dimensions for this are 1300mm wide and 1800mm deep.

Finishes and fittings are very important. The essentials are panelled surfaces with all pipework covered; strong, easily cleaned wash-basins, lavatory pans and urinals; mirrors over every wash-basin; shelves in both men's and women's lavatories for putting personal belongings on; good lighting; good ventilation; foolproof towel and soap dispensers and shaving points for men. In many cases a shower cubicle will be a welcome addition. Where the female population of the office is 10 or more, a rest room is desirable. This should not be regarded as a necessary nuisance, but carefully located, however small it may be, in a private position, with pleasant furniture and decoration. Care taken here will help to persuade staff that the firm's concern for them extends beyond the quality of typewriters and equipment provided for their work.

Catering and cleaning

Even minimum catering such as making coffee or tea can be wrongly regarded as a nuisance rather than something that can positively help staff in their daily routine. Of course, many existing offices do not have the space or the staff for elaborate facilities for cooking and washing up, and in this case a vending machine for hot drinks may be the answer. But with careful planning a small space can often be provided where simple catering can take place. The diagram on page 31 shows how this might be done. Quite apart from preparing drinks, it may be worth considering having a small refrigerator and other storage so that simple lunch-time snacks can be prepared. Many small companies have offices in neighbourhoods with few eating-places and this encourages the increasing popularity among staff of bringing their own lunch. A small but pleasant staff lunch room with the simple facilities mentioned above can therefore be very attractive and cost effective. Energy and time saved by not queueing at restaurants means fresher staff during the afternoon, and a welcome saving of money on their part.

Space for cleaners' equipment is quite a separate consideration, but it must not be overlooked. What is essential is a good-sized cupboard to take all brooms, vacuum cleaners and floor cleaning equipment – about 0.7 × 1.0m in plan will be perfectly adequate – with a cleaner's sink where mops and cloths can be rinsed. If this is not kept separate, cleaning equipment invariably gets mixed up with other storage, and lavatory hand basins will be cracked by heavy buckets or mops. It is important to get this sorted out at the start.

Storage space

This is much neglected at the early stage, either being forgotten entirely or underestimated, which is a pity because it often radically disrupts planning later on.

Detailed planning of storage space demands careful assessment of:

1 The range, quantity, sizes and weights of things to be stored.
2 The rate of consumption by the office as a whole of those things.
3 The frequency of consumption by individuals or work groups.

From such a review a decision can be made as to the comparative proportions of storage to be provided centrally in bulk, and locally in small quantities.

Where daily consumption of stock by one person exceeds that which can conveniently be stored in his/her desk then, to avoid constant movement to the central store, a further storage cabinet is required near that desk. It may be said that this is fairly obvious, yet experience shows that this simple fact is very frequently ignored until the new desk or new office is occupied, whereupon more furniture and more space is required.

The rate at which stock is used by the office as a whole naturally determines the size of a central store. This becomes the buffer between outside suppliers and each individual stock consumer in the office and is essential if a ready supply is to be ensured at a moment's notice. For convenience, this store should be fairly close to the entrance to the office. It does not need natural light but should be gently ventilated and, of course, absolutely dry. Some materials used in the office are sensitive to light or heat so that it is better if the room is unheated and not used for some other purpose – for instance, as a boiler or plan printing room. The walls and floor of a central store may be subjected to considerable loading and early thought should be given to their capacity and also to the types of storage methods (eg shelving, racks, bins etc) that are to be used in it.

Different offices need very varied amounts and types of storage – often peculiar to the business involved. Solicitors store deed boxes, architects their drawings, reprographic and data processing systems have their own software needs which are sometimes considerable. Variations in sizes of paper and forms and of equipment make quick assessment of storage needs difficult and built-in flexibility is obviously an advantage. Filing is usually by far the most demanding in terms of space and various systems are discussed in Section Six. Bulk storage of stationery is better handled by means of built-in units because separate cabinets become heavy, static and, hence, inflexible. 'First reserve' storage cabinets of moderate size can be used for heavy day-to-day needs and these can match other furniture.

One important storage need is for clothing – very often underestimated and a problem when wet. Most staff prefer to have clothes close at hand, and coat rails should allow about 150mm per person in length and be at least 1370mm from the floor.

Another important item is that of books. These are heavy and will need to be protected from dust and heat. The choice between a cabinet and open shelving will depend on the value of the books and how often they are consulted. Other items which may have to be stored include samples, tools, furniture and sometimes partition components. The table on page 32 will act as a check-list when considering storage and assessing space needs.

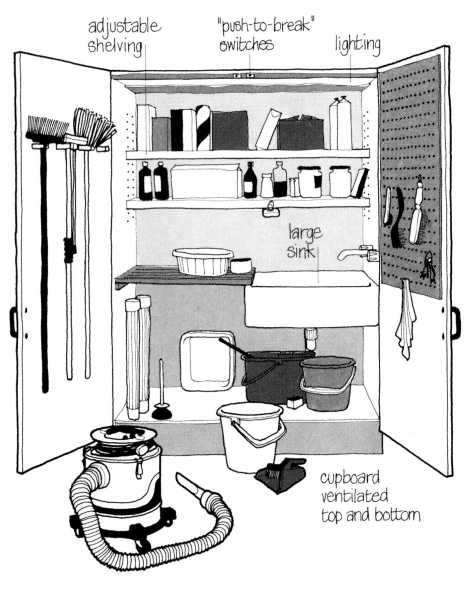

adjustable shelving

"push-to-break" switches

lighting

large sink

cupboard ventilated top and bottom

Small-scale office catering facilities can be provided without going to the length of having a separate kitchen. Here a deep recess in the wall of a lunch room has been used to provide the basic cooking necessities. Excellent ventilation is essential.

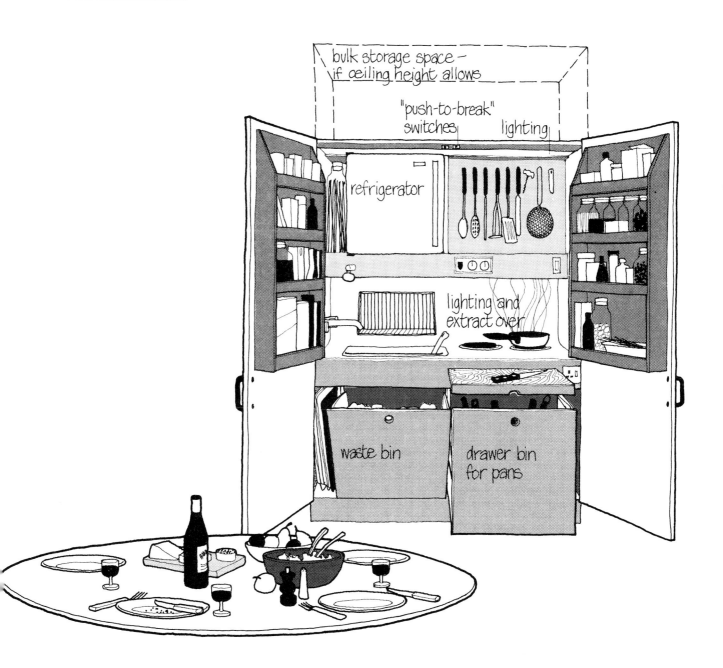

bulk storage space – if ceiling height allows

"push-to-break" switches

lighting

refrigerator

lighting and extract over

waste bin

drawer bin for pans

Corridors

Corridors are modest spaces whose purpose is solely functional. But a little thoughtful planning can make them interesting and perhaps rather more useful. Long, narrow, straight corridors are depressing: they should certainly never be less than 1200mm wide and preferably nearer 1500mm to allow people to pass easily and stop and chat. The occasional bay, say 1800mm long by 600mm deep, can form a convenient recess acting as a small entrance area to other offices, a place for a painting or an indoor plant, or simply to relieve uniformity. Doors should never open out into corridors except from very infrequently used rooms, and even then should be capable of being fixed back to avoid the danger created to passers-by. Lighting and colour can do a good deal to make corridor space pleasant and older people and the ambulant disabled will appreciate a handrail running down one side.

Office storage

★ = Lockable

Columns grouped under **LOCAL STORAGE** (Desk drawers and cupboards – Desk-top trays) and **CENTRAL STORAGE** (Special room – Sacks).

	Desk drawers and cupboards	Separate cabinets	Special cabinets	Filing cabinets	Filing trolleys	Central filing	Local shelving	Desk-top trays	Special room	Special cupboard	Refrigerator	Safe	Adjustable open shelving	Fixed open shelving	Tote boxes	Bins	Racks	Sacks
Stationery up to A4 size		x						x					★					
Smaller stationery items	x														x			
Larger stationery items			x													x		
Typing supplies		x														★		
File covers and boxes		x											x					
Copying paper			x							★								
Microfilm or tapes	x									★								
Drawing office supplies			x				x								★		x	
Printouts and punch cards																	x	
Print paper			x															
Special equipment (eg surveying)									★									
Drawings and plans			x							x								
Literature and catalogues			x				x						x					
Cleaning equipment and materials										★								
Coats, hats, bags and shoes			★															
Cash and valuables	★											★						
Confidential documents	★		★							★								
Work in progress	★																	
Samples															x	★	★	★
Rubbish																x		x
Food and drink											x							
Light bulbs, soap, towels etc																★		
First aid										x								
Spare furnishings										★								
Furniture and partitioning									★									
Tools										★								
Dead files and records														x				
Current filing				x	x	x												

TOP LEFT AND RIGHT *These examples show that even in a modern office, basic storage needs can be underestimated, wrongly positioned or simply forgotten!*

BELOW *The ingenious use of simply constructed, high-level shelving in this architects' office exploits all the available space and avoids the use of free-standing filing cabinets.*

Checklist: planning in detail

1	2	3	4	5	6	7
Has a clear decision to proceed to detailed planning been taken as a result of the feasibility study?	Who must have confidential enclosed space? Who does not need enclosed space? What tasks generate noise? What frequency of movement takes place between individuals or groups? What traffic of paperwork takes place between individuals or groups? What internal telephone calls take place? What other factors are there affecting the location of individuals or groups?	Has a layout for individuals and groups been arrived at using 'balloon' diagrams?	Have partitioned spaces been defined in principle? Have open-plan spaces been defined in principle?	Has the layout been checked relative to fire escape routes required by the Fire Officer?	Have detailed plans been arrived at for: Entrance/Reception Private offices Meeting rooms Executive offices Secretarial offices Corridors Open spaces Catering/Cleaning Lavatories Rest rooms Storage	Has a final layout of each space been produced in plan form, subject only to further investigation for environmental and technical servicing and equipment requirements?

SECTION THREE: *services and communications*

Importance of services

However well planned the rest of an office may be, it will succeed or fail according to the quality of its services and communications. In some ways this is the old problem of the chicken and the egg. Those fortunate enough to build from scratch can ensure that space and servicing needs are properly co-ordinated. Many firms, however, will take space in existing buildings where heating, lighting, power and ventilation installations are already established and working. These may affect detailed planning in ways that are not always obvious to the layman, who tends to see office layout in the more tangible terms of size and available facilities.

Some services, notably lighting, electric power and telephone systems, can usually be modified without too much difficulty. On the other hand, heating, ventilation and air-conditioning are much harder to alter, generally speaking. Service installation costs are high, so underestimating needs for services can result in serious budgetary problems, or perhaps an inadequately serviced office. Well designed furniture and equipment cannot possibly compensate for bad lighting, heating and ventilation, or insufficient electric points and telephones. Close attention to these matters is therefore needed at the planning stage.

Heat gains and losses

In fact, user surveys have shown that heating and ventilation are often the major sources of dissatisfaction in offices. The quality of heating, regardless of the method used, depends on the volume of air to be heated; how quickly it will lose or gain heat through outside walls or windows; how much heat will be gained from people in the room, from lighting and equipment; and how often the air will be changed by natural or forced ventilation. Heating can never be divorced technically from ventilation. Engineers actually express heating levels by referring to the temperature level to be achieved at an expected number of air changes per hour, relative to the outside air temperature. The trouble is that engineers' calculations, made when the building is designed, cannot anticipate later structural changes or the vagaries of human behaviour. For instance, a decision to upgrade lighting levels may produce considerably more heat with no corresponding balance in heat losses. Sometimes new partitions will have the effect of cutting off radiators from other parts of an office. Then there is the fresh air fiend who insists on open windows all the year round while sitting next to a convector fire. All these will certainly confuse the best possible estimates.

The heating of spaces is best compared to a cash balance sheet. On the income side is the heat emitted by all the sources of heat, including people in the room, while on the expenditure side are the heat losses. A balance has to be struck between the two and maintained regardless of changes in layout, numbers of personnel, lighting or ventilation. Even detailed design changes can alter space heating levels and distribution. Changes in radiator grilles, for example, will affect the heat radiated, and curtains and blinds can modify heat losses through windows. The heat of the sun is often disregarded, but an office with a large expanse of windows facing roughly south will get a lot of solar heating all year round, and particularly in summer. If offices facing in this direction have been partitioned off and air movement is reduced, the build-up of heat can be considerable. Blinds and curtains will only reduce heat gain marginally in such a case and ventilation fans can improve things only if air can be drawn through from the cooler side of the building.

Acceptable heating levels

Acceptable office heating levels have tended to increase in Britain over the past few years, principally because people now wear lighter, less formal clothing. Whereas the Offices Shops and Railway Premises Act of 1963

Heat gains and losses

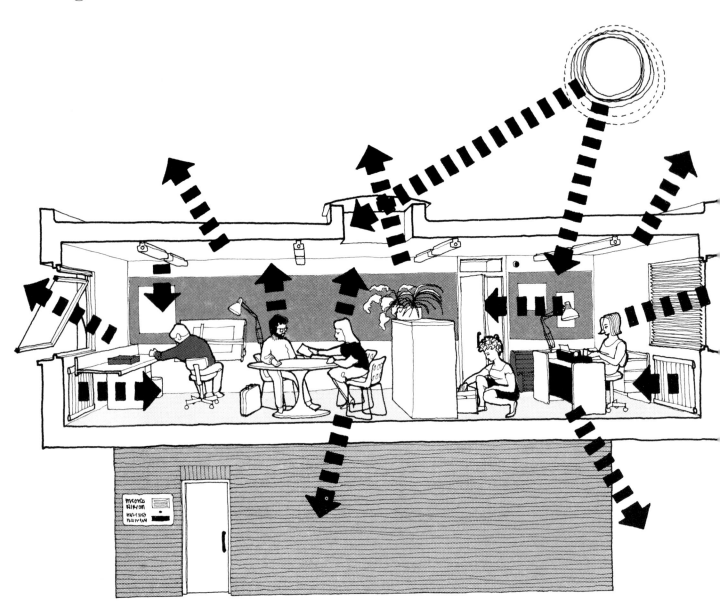

So-called radiators give out at least 50 per cent of their heat by convection, but it is the loss of radiant heat that appears significant when a radiator is masked by a piece of furniture. There is generally a greater fall-off in air temperature from floor to ceiling level and adjoining windows than with other types of heating. A radiator beneath a window helps to counteract down draught, but will lose heat to the outside wall unless an insulated backing is used.

Convection heating relies on natural air flow and gives a relatively even room temperature, especially if fittings are continuous below windows and if the room is draught fee. A fan-assisted convector has the same characteristics, but will positively counteract draughts and is controllable in output. Fans can be noisy and disturbing unless regularly maintained.

Mechanically ducted warm air is centrally heated (and is filtered and humidified in full air conditioning) and then introduced into the office space under very slight pressure through wall or ceiling grilles. Well designed ducting usually eliminates all noise from the central mechanical plant. If the partition and furniture layouts are compatible, such a system will ensure an even temperature throughout the office.

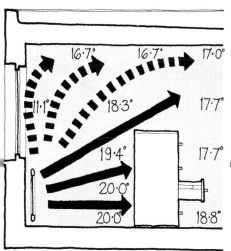

Radiator

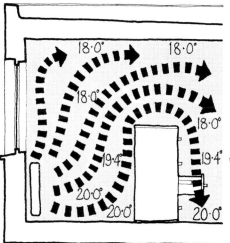

Convector

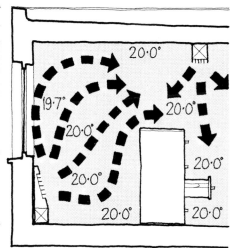

Ducted air

requires that a minimum of 16°C must be achieved after the first hour, we would now generally expect ambient air temperatures in the region of 18 to 21°C. The Act says that a thermometer must be provided 'in a conspicuous place' so that temperatures can be checked, but a thermometer may give a wholly wrong impression, because temperature level can vary considerably between floor and ceiling, depending on the type of heating used. Radiant heating will usually give a more even

temperature between floor and ceiling in the average office up to about 3m high than will a purely convection system. Fan assisted convection, while agreeably quick in warming up a space, can produce warm feet and cool shoulders. Heat distribution across the depth of a room usually varies slightly, although in the infrequent cases where floor or ceiling heating is used the temperature distribution will be evenly distributed horizontally. Temperatures may, of course, also be modified by external factors. An

unheated adjoining floor or proximity to the roof or garage space will cause greater than average heat loss. Finally, it is as well to remember the human factor. Different age groups react differently to temperature, and older people may very well feel cold when the temperature is acceptable to others.

Enough has been said to show that heating an office is a complex matter, and indeed the heating engineer will be as concerned with the standards decided upon (and discussed in Section One) as will the

Compact, gas-fired, convector space-heating units are available in a variety of sizes — wall mounted, thermostatically controlled (even in the event of an electricity cut) and easily regulated to suit individual office needs. They can provide a sensible alternative to a central heating system for smaller office areas, provided that balanced flues can be installed for each unit.

Smaller offices may find that off-peak electric storage systems are a convenient and economic form of heating. This model is wall mounted and only 120mm deep. Some units combine off-peak storage with normal electric convection heating, which can be used for rapid warmth when required, even when the storage section is not in use.

These hot water radiators are made in aluminium and are stove enamelled. Heat from the interior radiator is dissipated directly upwards and also horizontally by two layers of vertical fins. This enables a high heat output with a flat, 'touchable' external surface.

Heating units positioned around the perimeter of an office often look cumbersome and make partitioning difficult. One way of overcoming this is shown here, where standard modular casings are clipped together. This provides visual continuity and allows a neat joint with any partitions abutting the window. Power outlets are positioned at frequent intervals in the floor surface.

architect/designer. Two important and fundamental factors should, however, be noted before making a decision on what method of heating to use, since both can considerably affect running costs.

The effect of construction on heating

The first factor is that of the nature of construction of the building. A traditional 'heavy' building acts as a thermal reservoir: it takes a long time to heat up or cool down, and therefore shows a time lag in its reaction to changes in the weather. In such a building it is economically sensible to maintain heating input steadily during the heating season (generally from mid October to late April). Some smaller offices may be in 'lightweight' structures, or even prefabricated buildings. Buildings of this sort heat up and cool down in phase with the outside temperature however well they are insulated. They therefore need a heating system with a quick response.

The effect of heating method

The second factor concerns the way in which air inside the building is heated. This can be in any of three ways: by means of radiant surfaces; by convection; or by mechanically ducted air. Each has advantages and disadvantages in particular cases, and there is no 'best buy'. The table opposite indicates the characteristics that might be experienced with various types of installation for an office of 20 to 30 people, but actual performance will depend upon size, situation and usage, and a written statement by a competent heating engineer of both capital and running costs should therefore be obtained.

Heating systems

E=Excellent
G=Good
M=Moderate
P=Poor

	RADIANT							CONVECTION				MECHANICAL		
	Hot water radiators	Oil-filled electric heaters	Electric off-peak storage heaters	Wall panels	Skirting units	Under-floor heating	Ceiling panels	Skirting units	Under-cill units	Internal wall units	Fan-assisted units	Ducted air	High velocity ducted air	Air-conditioning
Flexibility relative to layout changes – open office	M	G_1	P	P	P	E	E	P	G	P	M/G	M	M	E
Flexibility relative to layout changes - closed office	P	E_1	P	P	M	E	P	P	G	P	M/G	P_5	P_5	P_5
Ease of extension of system or units	P/M	E_1	G_1	P	P	P	M	P	P	P	M/G	M	M	M
Speed of response to temperature change	G	G	P	G	G	G	G	G	G	G	E	E	E	E
Uniformity of vertical heat distribution	G	G	G	G	G	G	M/G_4	G	M	P	G	E	E	E
Uniformity of horizontal heat distribution	G_2	G_2	G_2	G_2	G_2	G	M	G_2	M	P_2	G	E	E	E
Freedom from dust staining	M	M	M	M	M	P	P	M/G	E	E	G	E	E	P_6
Quietness of system	E	E	E	E	E	E	E	E	E	E	M	M	P/M	G_7
Freedom from office noise transmission	M	E	E	E	M	E	E	P	P/M	G	E	M	M	M/E
Economy in operation	M	P	G	M	M	M_3	M_3	M	M	M	M/G	M/G	G	G

1 subject to electric loading capacity
2 subject to not being blocked by screening or furniture
3 assuming first class insulation beneath or above
4 subject to height of room not exceeding 3 metres
5 unless variations provided for during design
6 assuming filtration is part of conditioning
7 assuming central system (room units can be noisy)

Electric lighting

The quality of office lighting has also improved in recent years. Minimum lighting levels are laid down by the Offices Act, but the Illuminating Engineering Society (IES) publishes a code containing (among other valuable advice) recommendations for lighting intensities for specific tasks. These include:

Clerical tasks	500 lux
Typing pools	750 lux
Drawing offices	750 lux
General offices	500 lux

'Lux' is a measurement of light intensity (lumens per square metre) and provides a way of comparing light intensities (using a light meter), but *not* lighting quality. For instance, the light intensity out of doors on a bright sunny day might be about 10,000 lux, but this figure gives no indication of the shadows, colour and warmth provided by the moving clouds and sunlight. It needs little imagination to realise the effect which the somewhat elusive quality of lighting can have on the office. Some definition is possible, however, provided that it is understood that quality is an amalgam of many things – the type of light source, the design of light fittings, the background contrast, and the kind of surfaces on which the light falls and from which it is reflected.

In addition, office lighting must be flexible in operation, control and layout. Room sizes and desk positions are sometimes changed, and lighting arrangements should be able to cope with this. Different people in an office may also work different hours, so the lighting must be able to be reduced in an area where there are only one or two staff working.

Fluorescent lighting

In general, the choice of type of office lighting is still effectively between the incandescent 'light bulb' and the fluorescent 'tube', with minor variations of each on the side lines. Fluorescent tubes have become the accepted light source in general office areas in recent years because they offer a number of specific advantages for office use. They are, in fact, more costly to install, simply because the fittings are more complicated and expensive. But they are cheaper to run, give even, shadowless lighting and (of less importance except for very big installations) emit less heat than incandescent lighting. Fluorescent tubes are available in a number of lengths from 150mm to 2.4m, and they can be linked up in banks or rows to give very even, continuous, lighting conditions. They are also available in different colour renderings: the 'warmer' tubes are slightly less efficient but do provide a more pleasant light.

Lighting variation

A good deal of prejudice once existed against fluorescent lighting. It was considered factory-like, boring and characterless, and its stroboscopic 'flicker' was disturbing. Now better, more effective fittings are available and the flicker effect has been practically eliminated. Fluorescent light can be obtained not only from the customary tube (coded 'MCF' by manufacturers), but also from a large bulb (coded 'MBF') which screws into a socket holder in the same way as an incandescent lamp. This form is not yet widely used in offices, but it undoubtedly has a future because of its compact size.

The bulb is comparable in cost and efficiency to the tube. Lighting designers also now appreciate that people's eyes seek relief from the immediate task, however well lit, by concentrating occasionally on another, more distant view or on a different level of lighting, so that some variation in levels of light and different mixes of types of light can provide psychological benefit in creating visual interest. Areas or objects that have accents, contrast, shadow and form as a result of lighting therefore impart an important visual character to the office scene.

Lighting layout and flexibility

Ceiling lighting must be laid out keeping several requirements in mind and very often some compromise will be necessary. The lighting engineer will try to achieve a layout that gives a known, even intensity of light throughout the office, with no 'falling off' in isolated areas. The architect, on the other hand, will want to ensure that the fittings themselves will not inhibit future changes in partitioning, and he will be more concerned with the quality of the lighting, as it relates to interior design and colour. Both experts will, or should be, interested in switching arrangements – is it necessary for all the general office lighting to be kept on at great expense just because a couple of people work late occasionally? Can the last person to leave the office at night retreat in good order without having to do so in pitch darkness? Tube or bulb replacement is also important: if a standard fitting is used throughout the office, replacement, storage and fitting are all made easier. Many large offices replace all tubes at set intervals to save storage and labour costs.

Flexibility in lighting layout and design can be achieved by the use of one of the several tracking or trunking systems available. These enable various kinds of lighting sources to be clipped to a continuous track fixed either to, or above, the ceiling. The tracked systems can carry up to four separate circuits, so that four independently controlled areas or lighting functions can be adopted. Special care must be given to switching arrangements because there is a natural tendency to extend the coverage of tracked circuits over too large an area.

Glare

The quality of light has to do not only with the light source, but also with the way in which it is diffused, its background and the surfaces upon which the light falls. It is most important that the light source – fluorescent or incandescent – should not be directly visible from the work position, as this creates glare.

Shading devices are essential to diffuse the light and tone it down to moderate brightness. In some installations, and particularly with low ceilings, these diffusers are not always successful in shielding the eyes from the glare of the light source, and considerable eyestrain can result. (The archetypal newspaper reporter wearing a green eye-shade and crouched over a typewriter beneath a 200 watt unshaded light bulb is an extreme example!) Flush, ceiling-mounted fittings are natural offenders in this

Lighting

LEFT *Variation in lighting levels can add interest and visual quality to a room. In this case, the general lighting is provided by two flush-mounted ceiling fittings, while perimeter lighting illuminates the noticeboard and wall decorations. Anybody using the desk will face away from the window, which could cause uncomfortable glare were it not for the vertical blinds. A small desk light might be useful in overcoming the reduction in backlighting on dark evenings.*

BELOW *The suspended ceiling in this office combines glare-free lighting, acoustic panels, air conditioning inlets (with outlets through light fittings recirculating waste heat) and it also provides support for partitioning. The same ceiling system is used throughout, for both enclosed and open offices.*

RIGHT *Plastic diffusers are not always successful in reducing glare. Visual discomfort will be greatest on dull winter days or evenings when the contrast between bright lights and dark ceilings will be even more marked.*

BELOW *The ceiling in this office is lit partly by light reflected from the walls and the light-coloured worktops, and partly by daylight from the windows. This avoids an uncomfortable degree of contrast between the ceiling itself and the fluorescent lighting set flush in it behind diffusers. Such conditions are not always easily achieved, and it may be necessary to direct light onto the ceiling in order to prevent the glare which occurs when high-intensity lighting is viewed against a poorly lit background.*

respect, and several fittings designed for direct ceiling mounting employ flat plastic diffusers that only barely moderate the harshness of the light source, so they should be avoided. Some fittings enable the light source to be seen more easily from one angle than another so they must be installed in the most favourable position. One solution is to have a suspended ceiling with lighting set well back above it with a grid of some kind that diffuses the light as it passes through the ceiling plane. Such lighting grids or slots

sometimes double up as return inlets for air-conditioning. This kind of installation is ideal where there is sufficient height for a suspended ceiling, such as in converted warehouses and similar buildings.

The colour and texture of interior surfaces can also induce indirect glare. A dark ceiling or wall will accentuate the brightness of a light fitting and recessed ceiling lights can fail to illuminate the ceiling plane itself, which will thus appear dark in contrast to the light source. To avoid this the ceiling should be light in

colour and be lit by light 'spill' from elsewhere. The working surface itself is, of course, supremely important when considering good lighting conditions. A shiny, light-coloured desk surface reflecting high intensity lighting is optically disastrous, but many executive boardrooms suffer from exactly this defect. For the average work task a compromise must be reached between the immediate need to reduce reflected glare and the need for good lighting on the work itself. Angles are important here: for example, an architect needs plenty of light but works on white, slightly reflective paper. His drawing board is therefore suitably inclined so that light falling onto it is reflected away from his eyes. A comparison of matt and shiny typewriter keys also illustrates this point. On normal desk surfaces, therefore, a medium matt surface with, if possible, a slight texture, will serve most purposes. The hammered leather desk top, beloved by some executives, is very effective from this point of view.

Human considerations

Beyond these overall guiding principles for lighting there are other, human considerations. Older people tend to need more light, and to ignore this can cause problems. In smaller offices, a general level of background lighting can if necessary be supplemented by personal desk lamps, but this can be a nuisance in open-plan offices where desk space may be at a premium.

Lighting for other areas, including circulation areas, lavatories, rest

Overhead lighting track provides simple, yet infinitely variable lighting.

44

rooms and receptions, must be very carefully considered. Safety is particularly important in these cases, and very pronounced changes in intensity between different areas should generally be avoided.

Power and telecommunication outlets

Sufficient and convenient power and telecommunications outlets are essential to any office, particularly with the increased use of electrically operated office equipment. Power supplies are normally provided by means of socket outlets inset into walls or into a skirting duct around the perimeter of the office, with an occasional outlet on central column positions. However, this does not always allow easy access where desks are positioned in the middle of the floor space. With larger open offices, where desk and screen positions are likely to be changed or re-grouped, there should ideally be floor socket outlets at frequent intervals – 1200 to 1800mm is ideal. This is not only expensive, but is only really practicable if new building or substantial reconstruction is being carried out, because special ducts and outlets with hinged lids or 'turrets' are needed. Where there is a space above a ceiling, special trunking (similar to that used in factories) or high-level sockets can be used with flexes dropping down to different work positions. This is a good deal

less costly, but involves trailing wires, which can have obvious disadvantages. Perimeter power outlets at waist or ceiling level are sometimes useful, although in the latter case they will be difficult for people to reach. Low-voltage cables, such as those for telephones, can be run separately under floors, below new floor surfaces or even in the ceiling. This is not permitted for high-voltage cables, which must run in proper ducting to eliminate the danger of accidental penetration or damage.

Lifts

Lifts are another important service if access to the office depends on them. There is a curious tendency to economise on lifts, although this can positively waste time and money. The capacity and speed of lifts are critically important at peak hours of opening, closing and lunch breaks. The length of waiting times should be considered; this is, in effect, the total time for a round trip – assuming a reasonable time for stopping, discharging, and taking on the total passenger load for each

Offices lit by fluorescent tubes will be virtually shadowless unless directional lighting is introduced to give emphasis and contrast. Some schemes totally avoid fluorescent lighting and use only incandescent light sources; this executive office shows the softer and more varied illumination which can be achieved in this way, at rather greater operating cost.

Many people prefer a light source close to their work, but desk lamps can take up valuable space and prove a nuisance. This furniture/screening system incorporates a lighting unit that is adjustable in height above the work surface and diffuses upwards and downwards.

Special circumstances sometimes necessitate the adoption of a raised floor beneath which service cables, pipes and air ducts can be accommodated. To provide access to these services a floor can be

formed of modular steel panels (covered by a variety of finishes) supported by steel legs on the structural floor beneath. This installation is in a computer room.

floor, divided by the total number of lifts. There are many factors to assess when checking the adequacy of a lift installation: the number of floors being served; the population of each floor; other goods and passengers that have to be carried, and so on. Correlating these factors is the job of the lift engineer, who may need to be consulted about existing or new installations.

Fire and burglar alarms

Fire alarms, burglary alarms and fire-fighting equipment are essential, but often neglected, services. Prevention is better than cure, and the importance of reducing fire hazards is referred to elsewhere in this book. Fire Officers normally specify the numbers and types of fire extinguishers to be installed; alternatively, hose reels connected to

the water mains may be needed where several floors of office space are involved. Dry chemical or vaporising liquid extinguishers are available where water damage must be avoided at all costs. Where documents or articles of exceptional value are kept in the office, special fire alarm bells actuated by heat or smoke can be installed and connected directly to the local fire station. Smoke or heat detectors positioned within or close to articles of special value can also trigger off an alarm in the office. Similarly, burglar alarms can be installed, either to trigger a bell outside the building (often disregarded in practice) or connected directly to the police station. The police and insurance companies can give advice on these important matters and on security generally.

Planning telecommunications

Efficient telecommunications systems are vitally important to every size of office and should be planned at the same time as the other services. Cable ducts and equipment space must be properly designed and co-ordinated with any other building works. This is rarely the case, simply because a telecommunication system tends to be regarded as 'equipment' which can be added when the office is otherwise complete. This is a mistaken view and it usually means added expense in the longer term.

The Post Office itself says that 'the problem of concealing all PO cables and wires, while similar in many respects to that confronting other services, is slightly more complicated by the necessity of having to provide telephones at any

Both lighting and power are available in this architect's studio (converted from an old printing works) by plugging in to an overhead supply. Such an installation can give great flexibility at relatively low capital cost.

The decision whether or not to employ fire detectors in an office will depend on the degree of fire risk and the chances of detecting a fire in its early stages. The characteristics of the space will determine which kind of detector to use: either a heat-sensitive type (left below) or a smoke detector (right below). Both actuate an alarm or relay a call to the fire brigade.

desired position in the building at short notice. . .' The Post Office should therefore be approached as soon as floor plans are available and regarded as consultants.

They will base their advice upon the type of business, the number of staff, frequency of telephone usage, the layout of the office and the likelihood of expansion. Connection and alteration charges can be considerable, so it is usually in the user's interest to overestimate slightly at the outset. A very wide range of systems and apparatus is available and it is too extensive to describe here except in very general terms. The most elementary small office will certainly be served by one or more exchange lines each connected to one telephone instrument. Elaboration of such a service depends on the individual needs of each office in sorting, transferring and routing internal and external calls.

The first step of elaboration enables the extension of one or several exchange lines to be shared by a small number of people working in different positions. The Post Office refers to these extension arrangements as 'plans' or 'keymasters', each of which they code according to the facility it gives.

Private branch exchanges

Where these arrangements will not provide the flexibility or scope required, the office must consider the installation of a Private Branch Exchange (PBX). This exchange, operated within the office, enables the provision of a chosen number of extensions, central monitoring of incoming calls and the opportunity of internal telephone

communication. In principle two distinct types of PBX are available: either a Private Manual Branch Exchange (PMBX) or a Private Automatic Branch Exchange (PABX). Both systems require an operator/supervisor, though not necessarily continuously.

The use of the word 'manual' in PMBX implies that interconnections between exchange lines and extensions, or between internal extensions, can normally only be made via the switchboard by an operator. If the operator is absent then each exchange line can be switched through to a selected extension which then performs as if it were a separately connected telephone capable of receiving and making external calls direct. Calls cannot then be transferred to another extension (unless, of course, the switchboard setting is modified again). A PMBX is normally best suited to offices with little or no need for internal telephone communications because when this need does arise, the switchboard operator is obliged to make the connection. This could interrupt other work upon which he or she is engaged, such as typing or reception, and can become uneconomic. If frequent internal telephone conversation is required then either a separate internal telephone system or a private automatic branch exchange should be installed. A valuable variation to a PMBX system is possible by applying some of the 'plan' arrangements described above to selected PMBX switchboard extensions. This simply means that, using for instance, Plans 1 and 1A, several people can communicate

with one another and make and receive calls on any of the telephone instruments connected to the PMBX. The Post Office does not recommend this system on other than lightly used extensions.

The use of the word 'automatic' in PABX implies that interconnections between exchange lines and extensions, or between internal extensions can be made directly from any telephone connected to the PABX switchboard. This is done by means of an internal dialling code system whereby each extension is given a distinguishing code number; an exchange line is usually obtained by dialling '9'. Thus the switchboard operator is by-passed and need only receive and handle incoming calls, routing them to the appropriate person. A PABX is normally best suited to offices which have very heavy telephone traffic because it reduces the work of the switchboard operator and allows quick internal telephone connections.

Although a wide range of standard private manual and automatic switchboards are available 'off the shelf', the Post Office and approved private contractors can arrange special variations of these standard switchboards to cater for particular needs. All private branch exchanges require space to accommodate the switchboard itself, apparatus and power units. Some key operated switchboards can be mounted simply on a desk top; others consist of special floor mounted cabinets with cord cable plug operation. Apparatus varies in size from relatively small wall mounted units to heavy equipment needing special, carefully ventilated rooms.

A Private Manual Branch Exchange (PMBX) switchboard with two lines and six extensions, suitable for the smaller office.

The Key and Lamp Unit is a particularly useful alternative to a switchboard in offices where a call can be answered by any member of a working group. Incoming calls are signalled on every unit and can operate an audible signal as well.

This automatic telephone answering machine can be used to record incoming calls when an office is closed or the switchboard is unmanned. It can also be used to make a record of other important telephone conversations.

Key and lamp units

Some organisations, such as travel and ticket agencies, bookmakers and wholesalers, have constant heavy telephone traffic yet do not need a switchboard and operator because calls can be answered by any one of a group of people. For these situations the Post Office can provide 'key and lamp units' – small line switching units, made in two sizes with an accompanying telephone instrument, which sit on each desk in the group. Up to 10, or up to 20, exchange lines, or internal circuits, can be connected to the smaller or larger unit respectively; an incoming call on any circuit flashes a signal lamp on every unit and operates an audible alarm. The call can be answered, or referred, by any member of the group by moving a key on the unit. Outgoing calls can

also be made by any of the group members.

Internal systems which are entirely separated from the public exchange system are available from both the Post Office and independent contractors. These permit direct personal communication between people without the assistance of an operator on a private branch exchange system. They are particularly useful for conference calls between widely separated individuals. The effect of an internal telephone system is to double up on wiring, apparatus and instruments which is space consuming and may help to conceal a far more fundamental problem of spatial and locational organisation. For more immediate person to person contact, a direct speech connection is possible using a very

simple installation supplied by independent manufacturers whereby, simply by pushing a button and speaking towards an instrument, direct verbal contact is made. Lack of confidentiality and noise disturbance are the disadvantages, however.

Other useful telephone apparatus

Further apparatus available to supplement PO telephone systems is described below.

Press Button Keyphones. Telephone instruments with press button keys instead of dials; considered to be more accurate in usage than dialling. The keying process is quicker, although the connection time is the same as for dialling.

Callmakers. Names and telephone numbers are stored on punched card or magnetic tape (up to 400); cards

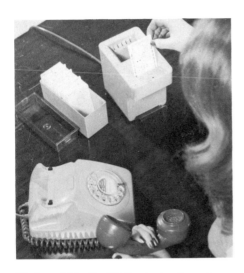

The Post Office Card Callmaker is a timesaving device which operates by means of punched cards, which can record up to 16 digits, and make calls automatically. Numbers are changed by punching a fresh card.

are fed by hand, or tape data, automatically into the callmaker which will then dial any stored number; enormously time-saving where large numbers of routine calls are made.

Loud speaking telephones. Desk units with loudspeakers and microphones in combined or separate units. They enable telephone conversations to take place without use of the telephone (used optionally) and with both hands free to deal with paper and notes.

Speaker sets. Small desk units which amplify incoming speech sufficiently to be heard by a small group of people or broadcast to an office. The larger of two units available requires mains power.

Answering sets. Desk-top units which connect to the telephone and, when actuated, automatically transmit a recorded message up to 20 seconds in length to the caller.

Metering facilities. Small meters connected to an exchange line telephone or PBX switchboard indicate the number of units used in a call or series of calls. They are useful for assessing the cost of STD calls but not suitable for checking total charges for all dialled calls.

Signalling devices. Range of different types of bell, buzzers, hooters, and lamp signals suitable for use in special situations; can supplement the normal telephone bells.

Private circuits. Provide continuous or part-time exclusive contact between two points either suitable for speech or non speech transmission (eg data facsimile, alarm controls etc). They cannot be interconnected with the public telephone network.

Facsimile transmission. Machines connected to the public telephone system which enable the transmission of data, text or even graphic material.

Telex

Telex installations are often not regarded as being of value to an office unless it is involved with exports. Yet, while use of telex between offices in the UK is still limited in scope, there can be no question that it has considerable advantages over telephone or postal services. Telex consists essentially of a teleprinter (which is similar to electric typewriter) in one office connected to a teleprinter in another. A message typed in one office by teleprinter is received exactly as it was sent and proof of receipt is endorsed, with date and time, on the message. Thus a telex message has the same legal authority as a letter with the added advantage of immediate, guaranteed delivery; messages can be received when the office is closed and are unaffected by the delays of weather or strikes. The space required for the teleprinter is no more than for a large typewriter and small desk (710×970× 1000mm high). The keyboard is simple and requires no special skills; a secretary can type directly during transmission or prepare a message on perforated paper tape for automatic high-speed transmission. The costs of stationery and stamps are thus eliminated and the labour costs are less than for a normal letter because only typing is involved. Telex installations are therefore most valuable where rapid, accurate response is required frequently. Connection charges, transmission charges and rental costs are relatively modest and, depending on frequency of use, can show an advantage over other systems.

Visual communication
The Post Office can also provide facilities for simultaneous visual/aural conferences to take place between custom-built studios in London, Birmingham, Bristol, Manchester and Glasgow. The charges are modest, for instance £60 for the use of two studios up to 200kms apart for 30 minutes. Savings in travelling costs and time can more than compensate for this.

The transmission of exclusively visual information is occasionally required by specialist users. Closed circuit television (CCTV) can be used to convey information within a building or between offices a short distance apart – for instance between the Stock Exchange and brokers' offices. The Post Office and private contractors can provide specially engineered CCTV circuits which, depending on the system adopted, can convey a certain degree of fine detail on drawings or documents. But a facsimile transmission system with special transmitters, receivers and/or viewers, can transmit documents up to a limited size over any distance using normal telephone circuits. The Post Office must be called upon at an early stage to advise whether circumstances will permit the use of such a system.

TOP RIGHT *The Teleprinter keyboard is almost identical to that of a typewriter. It is power assisted and a good typist can achieve 35 to 40 words a minute (though automatic transmission of a message will be at 70 words per minute). Messages are sent and received via the same unit. The chatter of the machine can be slightly disturbing, especially if it stands in a private office. A sound-reducing cover with a window through which messages can be read is available.*

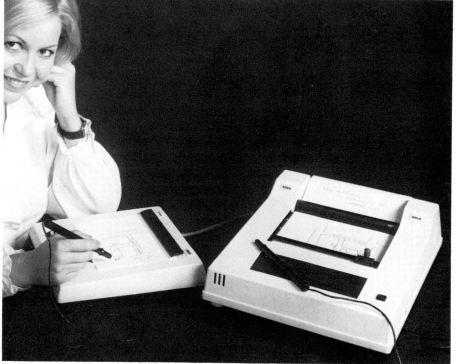

RIGHT *The Telenote transceiver consists of a roll of paper, special pens and the loudspeaking telephone equipment packaged in a unit measuring 406×305mm. The operator writes with a pen attached to the unit by a lightweight flex. The receiving transceiver's built-in pen reproduces the message or sketch as it is drawn. Telenotes can operate on telephone lines anywhere in the world, and are obviously useful for the rapid transmission of drawings or plans.*

SECTION FOUR: *the internal scene*

The effects of layout and services

Sections Two and Three of this book have discussed space layout and essential office services. These have a critical effect on the detailed interior design of the office, which is why they have to be considered first. But the sequence is not a rigid one and a good designer will from the first be aware of the visual impact of such components as partitions, radiators and fire escape routes.

Of course, part of the overall policy of the design may well be to project a particular image. Perhaps the lean efficiency of a production line is preferred to the hairiness of a country craft shop, or anonymity to blatant self-advertising. Whatever is required, walls, partitions, floor and ceiling surfaces and all the other elements of the internal scene must be examined and co-ordinated.

The influence of the building

Small office conversions possibly pose the most interesting and difficult problems, especially in fairly old buildings. At first sight, such conversions look daunting, however suitable these may be in terms of layout and services. Rooms seem impossibly high, staircases look gloomy, floors are uneven, and the extent of renovation may be limited by the lease. Unless the landlord will co-operate (and, one hopes, contribute) the designer faced with a short lease will have to restrict himself to using as many non-fixed items as possible, with decoration as the only non-recoverable item of expenditure. This approach will affect the choice of all the internal components – flooring, partitions, lighting, furniture and so on. A sensible designer will try to exploit any existing pleasant features, such as cornices, doorways and fireplaces, since these can add a lot to the interior at no extra cost. In contrast to older buildings, an early 1950s office floor will offer a dull, well constructed uniformity, ideally suited to the use of proprietary partitioning systems, strip lighting and wall to wall carpet. But its parallel lines of windows, hard internal finishes and long radiators sometimes present extremely difficult problems in terms of layout and acoustics. The designer may try to solve these by using textured or elaborate materials on walls and screens, and by creating visual interest with lighting or contrasting decoration at focal points. Different problems therefore suggest different approaches because the designer cannot impose his 'style' on any environment. Instead he will choose components and visual effects to modify and improve what already exists.

Essential visual factors

Before discussing the function of these components, let us look at some of the more important visual factors that must be kept in mind when assessing an interior. First, we must be constantly aware of the proportions of the spaces involved, especially in small offices. These will be considerably affected by furniture and screening, and by ceiling treatment and lighting. Next we must watch shape and form – the size and shape of internal columns and beams, or of staircase walls and partitions. The third factor is pattern, which affects apparent proportions and includes the patterns of lighting, ceiling tiles and repetitive partitions. A fourth factor, texture, is closely linked to pattern and can, in fact, itself create a repetitive pattern when used on ceiling tiles and curtains. Finally, we should be aware of colour and its correlation on desk tops, partition panels, floor coverings and walls.

Colour

This final factor, colour, deserves special mention because it is difficult to illustrate and assess. Also, apart from the colours in the office over which there is some control, there will be the colours of people's clothing, stationery and so on. Some people are less sensitive to colours than others – this is not a matter of colour blindness, it is much more a matter of early conditioning at school and at home – but those who

The apparent shortcomings of a late nineteenth-century shirt factory in London have been exploited here to create interesting and characterful offices. The existing ceiling was lined with open-jointed boarding over an absorbent material to make it *acoustically effective. Its height enables light to filter through glazed partitions and doors into the centre of the floor space. Cork tiles make a quiet, comfortable and easily maintained floor. The cast-iron column remains an interesting feature.*

are sensitive to colour seem to experience a definite physical reaction to colour. For instance, Miss Jones's maroon desk combined with the light green dress she always wears in spring may bring about actual nausea in the rest of the staff, the real cause of which may remain obscure.

For reasons such as this, strong colours are better avoided in an office, except perhaps as points of emphasis away from direct lines of sight. However, warm but not necessarily bright colours seem from experience to induce a sense of well-being. They are particularly useful as floor colours since mud and dust tend towards warmish brown. More neutral colours such as warm greys are useful as a background to the varying colours of furniture, equipment and clothing, although

they can become monotonous if used extensively in areas like corridors. For non-working areas, brighter, more varied schemes can be used.

Functional criteria

The main enclosing elements of the internal scene – floors, ceilings, walls and partitions – each contribute to its visual impact. Functional considerations will also have an important effect on the appearance of an office. How should one therefore select these elements? The criteria are extensive, but they can be summed up under the following:

1 Basic construction.
2 Fire resistance.
3 Effects of technical installations.
4 Wear resistance.
5 Ease of replacement.
6 Acoustic properties.
7 Cost of installation.

Basic construction

Section Seven discusses the various types of construction of office premises and how these can affect planning. Construction details also affect the way in which materials and components are installed and how they perform in use. For example, all buildings are more or less subject to movement, as a result of loading, ground movements, or even heating brought about by the heat of the sun. Non-flexible finishing materials must therefore only be used where such movement is unlikely.

It would be unwise, to take an extreme example, to use jointless terrazzo flooring on timber floor construction, and similarly, standard metal partitioning will almost certainly be difficult to install in an 18th-century building with floors bowed by age. Another consideration is the relative ease with which components can be fixed. A suspended ceiling can be installed beneath a timber floor with less noise and disruption than beneath a concrete one, for example. Solid structural walls can carry considerable loads in the form of safes, equipment or cupboards fixed to them, and they also form very effective barriers to airborne sound because of their mass. Non-structural walls, or partitions built of blockwork or timber framing, will be

Pattern can derive from less obvious items in the office, such as lighting and ceiling layout, carpet tiles and so on. In this office the curtains are the only deliberately designed pattern, yet they merge happily with the low-key rhythms induced by window blinds, plants and light fittings.

capable of taking only moderate loads and are less effective at reducing airborne sound, but they can be dismantled easily, although with a good deal of noise and dust.

The Building Regulations (see Section Eight) demand a certain degree of fire resistance for some materials used in the office. In addition to specifying the fire resistance of walls that divide up parts or areas of a building, there are stated levels of resistance to flame spread for all finishing materials used in fire escape routes, including staircases. Certain materials, notably plastics laminates, sheet vinyl, curtain materials and timber, must therefore be used with caution in escape areas. A plastic laminate may have to be bonded to a non-combustible material, entrance area displays may have to be in metal cases, and wall coverings may have to be in fire resistant materials. A wide range of fire resistant fabrics is now available, so choice is not too restricted.

Flame and heat are not the only hazards due to fire; asphyxiation from smoke and hot gases is also a danger, and many materials produce these in surprisingly large quantities. Ceilings are particularly hazardous. The voids above a

suspended ceiling can act as a horizontal flue and carry sparks and gases from one part of the office to another unless fitted with vertical fire stop baffles. Cheap polystyrene tiles stuck directly to an existing ceiling surface should be avoided since they emit quantities of black toxic smoke if they catch fire.

Technical installations
Interior finishes must allow reasonable access to cables, pipes and other technical installations in walls, floors and ceilings. There is

often a great temptation not to provide for this, so that when a service does need repair or modification, the process is disruptive and causes damage to the furnishings. A good maxim here concerning pipes and cables is 'if you can't get at them, put them on the surface'. Ducts should be provided wherever possible, with internal dimensions chosen to allow services to be fitted in and then bent or twisted to serve outlets. (This applies as much to thick electric cables as it does to pipes.) The effect

A relatively small room, in this case a meeting room, can be extended in visual scope by the intelligent co-ordination of pattern, form and lighting. Here the enclosing walls are reduced in scale by concentrating light onto a lively abstract painting and the patterned curtains. Shapes in the painting are echoed by the chairs, tables and the leaves of the palm. The carpet and upholstery are subdued in tone, which helps to direct visual attention outwards.

on finishes and components is obvious. Carpets must be fitted to allow for floor-level electric outlets, since office layout may well be dictated by these. Ceiling tiles should be removable where necessary. The position of wall outlets must be planned in advance and not left to chance. Finally, of course, the service outlets must be at least adequate for the job. Installing a single electric socket where two electric typewriters are likely to be used is a false economy.

Wear resistance

The criterion of wear resistance is an important one not only for flooring but also for other elements. Small spaces, narrow corridors and awkward plan shapes increase wear on flooring and also on walls which tend to be rubbed against at hand and shoulder height. Cleaning equipment, chairs and trolleys all have a considerable impact on walls, particularly at skirting level, and materials must be chosen with this in mind. Waist rails and skirtings are often a good idea and can form an interesting visual link between spaces if continued throughout the office. The wall covering itself is obviously important; soft materials like hessian or cork are not a good idea for walls subject to impact or abrasion, and hard, easily scratched materials may be equally unsuitable. Although ceilings are not subject to daily wear in the same way, they are affected from time to time by cleaners and service engineers, the latter being the greater menace. Lamp replacement seems inevitably to lead to dislodged tiles or grubby marks and the rougher the texture, the greater the

Two good examples showing ways in which materials chosen specifically to reduce maintenance have resulted in very different designs. On the left, stainless steel column casings, plate glass doors, marble skirtings and PVC clad walls project a glossy commercial image. On the right light grey mosaic walls, a white painted ceiling and a well designed umbrella stand suggest a steady professional attitude. Both examples fulfil their intentions admirably.

damage. It is therefore best to avoid using highly textured ceilings in areas liable to such abuse.

Ease of replacement

Replacement and redecoration are clearly associated with wear resistance. On the other hand, the replacement of components such as partitions may be entirely due to changes in the office layout. Whatever the reason, replacement and redecoration are bound to be disruptive unless they are carried out when the office is closed. Many leases demand redecoration at regular intervals, which is another reason for careful assessment. Smooth, hard finishes collect less dust than textured ones, and are more easily cleaned. However, an interior consisting entirely of plastic laminate, glass, ceramic tiles and chrome plate would be both visually and acoustically unsatisfactory as an office. Regular and conscientious (but not necessarily over-vigorous) cleaning and maintenance will immeasurably assist in reducing the need for refurbishing. Stopping dirt and dust entering the office by having good entrance mats and carpets will help here. Full air conditioning virtually eliminates airborne dust and reduces the need for heavy cleaning appreciably.

Offices of more than average height are spacious and pleasant, but the cost of redecorating them is high – a good reason for fitting a suspended ceiling; duller but cheaper in terms of running costs. One compromise is to design in such a way as to limit the area for decoration to about 2m above the floor. Below this some walls can be covered with panelling in the form of

Sound transmission

The heavier the materials used, the more effective they will be at reducing sound transmission through them (subject to there being no air passages such as keyholes, gaps in partitions and around doors). This diagram shows the approximate sound reducing qualities (in decibels) of various types of wall construction. Sound transmission through suspended ceilings and floors follows the same principles and must be considered in conjunction with the walls. Note that surface absorbent treatment does not affect the principle of transmission.

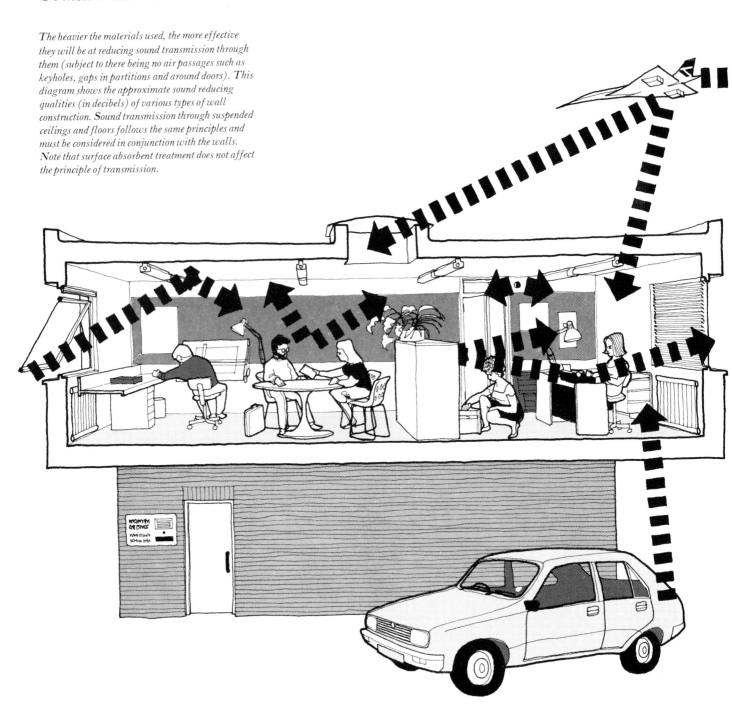

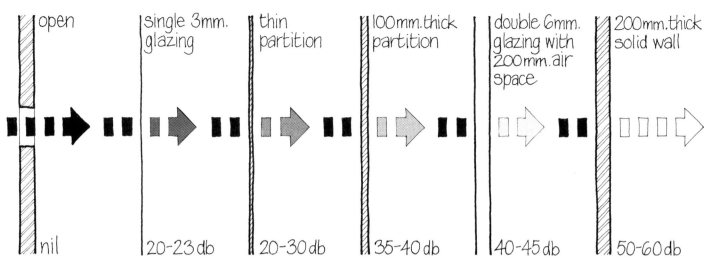

open	single 3mm. glazing	thin partition	100mm.thick partition	double 6mm. glazing with 200mm. air space	200mm.thick solid wall
nil	20-23 db	20-30 db	35-40 db	40-45 db	50-60 db

pin-boards or decorative materials, including curtains. Unfortunately, visually attractive materials often need redecoration or replacement more frequently than others. Textured surfaces, for instance, lose their pristine quality rather quickly as they collect dust, unless the space is air conditioned. Sheet vinyl materials tend to attract dust by electrostatic action, although they are quite easily cleaned. Some, but not all, carpet tiles can be easily moved or replaced, which can be a considerable asset. Dismantling and re-erecting partitioning systems is a subject in itself and is dealt with later on. However, it is worth noting that replacing partitions often damages or marks floor and ceiling finishes, which have to be made good afterwards.

Acoustics

Interior finishes also have a profound effect on acoustics, and this is one of the most difficult environmental factors to understand and anticipate. The subject is far too extensive to be covered fully in this general survey. Most people only become aware of sound when it reaches unacceptable levels and is damned as 'noise'. This is a significant distinction because, while we may all prefer a 'noise-free' office, it would be very uncomfortable to have a 'sound-free' one. Background noise comes from three main sources: first and most immediate is that made by colleagues; next is the noise from outside or the adjoining office that comes through windows, walls and doors; and finally, there is the noise made by equipment, mechanical heaters, fans and so on. If all the external and mechanical noise were to be eliminated (which can be done to some extent by using double glazing and having heavy walls), there would be no masking effect on the sounds of speech and movement. Every word would then be heard and seem unreasonably intrusive. For practical purposes, therefore, some degree of background noise or 'hum' is desirable as a basic acoustic 'climate'. Within the office, spaces can be 'tuned' by deflecting or absorbing unwanted sound created within them. It is also possible to tone down or attenuate sounds being transmitted from one space to another.

Most laymen are under the mistaken impression that acoustics can always be improved by using plenty of absorbent finishes – notably acoustic ceilings – but this is not necessarily true. Absorbent finishes vary in efficacy, and ceilings and carpet will, in any case, only *lower* general sound levels – not solve a particular noise problem in a given location. To do this, the acoustic climate may actually need the *addition* of a controlled sound input. Deflection or absorbtion of sound by means of screens may also be necessary. Where more privacy is required, partitions may have to be erected, and the sound attentuation of these will need special attention. The extent to which extra absorbent materials are introduced, and their position, depends very much on the area of hard, reflective materials in the room and the degree to which their effect can be modified. Large areas of glazing or hard plastered walls, for instance, may need curtaining or other softening

treatment. Finally, the actual volume of the office will determine the speed at which sound 'decays' as it moves out from its source. It should be clear by now that achieving good acoustic conditions is a complicated business, whether the office is large or small.

Cost

The last, but possibly the most important, criterion against which to evaluate materials is that of cost. Enough has been said already to show that a material that is cheap in itself can bring about considerable extra expense in installation and during its life. It is also fair to say that the most expensive materials and finishes are not necessarily the most efficient or appropriate ones. Sensible balances must be struck, and it is better to have critical parts of the office functioning well than put up with an inefficient overall compromise.

Floor finishes

A vast range of finishing materials exists from which those most suitable for the situation can be chosen, bearing in mind the criteria described above. Here we can only give a brief review of these and note significant characteristics. Let us start with floor finishes. These must be chosen with great care since they can be one of the most expensive interior elements, and one of the most heavily used. Movement routes across them cause uneven wear and this will soon be apparent unless the material used is hard and unyielding. Unfortunately, wear-resistant floor materials are often rather noisy in use. The table shows the characteristics of types of flooring that might be considered for parts of an office or its ancillary spaces. Of particular importance are carpets, which over the past 15 years have moved out of the boardroom and into the general office. Carpet is versatile, flexible material, available in a wide range of specifications. Its cost and durability relate primarily to the type of fibre or mix of fibres used and also upon its construction which can be woven (eg Wilton and Axminster), tufted, needle-punched or ribbed (corded). Office wear is heavy and ten years is an excellent life for a carpet classified as being for 'general contract use'. For even wear, carpet needs a smooth base free from ridges and bumps; the use of an underlay increases its life considerably as well as improving its acoustic and thermal insulation. Telephone wires and cables should not properly be run under it except in shallow ducts formed in the floor topping beneath the carpet.

Carpet tiles suit the needs of the smaller office admirably, since they can be moved round or replaced in order to even out wear or damage. However, some tiles 'creep', slide or wrinkle themselves out of position and need to be fixed with double-sided sticky tape or glue. It is a good idea to order about 10 per cent extra

Floor finishing materials

It is impossible to sum up every characteristic in this table, which should be regarded as a guide rather than as the basis for final choice. Some materials shown are rarely adopted in offices (eg acrylic and sisal carpet, mosaic or quarry tiles) but may be encountered or used in special situations. The cost base of 100 is indexed against a typical wool/nylon carpet simply because this is possibly the most common office flooring material in current use. Fire resistance and the electrostatic characteristics of different carpet materials can be improved by differing constructions and additives.

E=Excellent
G=Good
M=Moderate
P=Poor

	Cost Index	Appearance retention	Abrasion resistance	Non-slipperiness	Resilience	Sound absorption	Fire resistance	Electrostatic propensity	Ease of change	Ease of replacement	Ease of maintenance	Life
CARPET (TILE OR ROLL)												
Wool	55-145	G/E	G	E	E	E	M/G	M	E	E	E	P/M
Nylon	35-70	G/E	H	E	G	E	P	E	E	E	E	P/M
80% wool 20% nylon	55-105	G/E	G/E	E	G/E	E	P/M	E	E	E	E	P/M
Acrylic	35-55	M	G	E	G	E	P	E	E	E	E	P
Rayon blends	14-45	M	M	E	M/G	E	P	P	E	E	E	P
Polypropylene	15-45	M	E	E	M	E	P	P	E	E	E	P
Sisal	10-20	P/M	G	E	M	E	P	P	E	E	E	P
Manmade fibre/ animal hair blentl	45-60	P/M	P/G	E	E	E	P	M	E	E	E	P
SHEET OR TILE												
Rubber	70	G/E	G	E	E	G	P/M	E	P	P/M	E	G
Plastics covered cork	65	G	M/G	G/E	E	G	M	P	P	P/M	E	G
Natural cork	55	M/G	M	E	E	G	M	P	P	P/M	G	G
Linoleum	35	M	G	G	M	M	M	P	P	P/M	G	M
Flexible vinyl	25	P/M	G	G	M	M	G	P	P	P/M	G	M
WOOD												
Hardwood strip	115	M/G	G/E	M	M	P/M	M	P	P	P	M/G	E
Hardwood block	80	M/G	E	M	M	P/M	M	P	P	P	M/G	E
STONE AND CERAMIC												
Marble	535	E	E	P	P	P	E	P	P	P	G/E	E
Mosaic	115	E	G/E	P/M	P	P	E	P	P	P	G/E	G/E
Quarry tiles	55	E	E	P/M	P	P	E	P	P	P	G/E	E

for replacement purposes. Before carpet became popular, cork tiles were considered excellent for general office use and, apart from their relative permanency and dull colour, they still have much to offer. Those moving into an office with an old cork floor should have it cleaned off and resealed, after which it will be a first-class floor, although technical service runs cannot, of course, be accommodated easily. Very attractive plastic-sealed cork tiles are also available which keep their colour, are easy to clean and wear very well at a cost comparable to good carpet. Terrazzo or tile flooring may be considered for washrooms and lavatories in view of their good wearing qualities. They are not, however, suitable if the underlying structure is subject to movement, in which case vinyls or linos in tile or sheet form will be more suitable.

Ceiling finishes

Ceilings are particularly important in the office because, apart from anything else, they are the prime reflectors and distributors of natural and artificial light. A secondary, but important, role may be to provide fixing and support for partitions and support and concealment for services running above or below them. So, except where the ceiling is simply acting as a light source, its layout must be carefully planned so that partitions, lamps, air outlets and so on will function efficiently and perhaps be modified over the years, without interfering with one another. We have already seen that the ceiling is a convenient place in which to introduce absorbent material to help in providing a reasonable acoustic climate.

FAR LEFT *Carpet tiles made up from various proportions of man-made and natural fibres can be laid loose on flat, hard, non-slippery floors. They are extremely hard-wearing and easy to replace, as well as being relatively anti-static.*

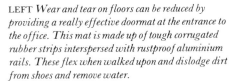

LEFT *Wear and tear on floors can be reduced by providing a really effective doormat at the entrance to the office. This mat is made up of tough corrugated rubber strips interspersed with rustproof aluminium rails. These flex when walked upon and dislodge dirt from shoes and remove water.*

Laying panels into a typical suspended ceiling grid, made of galvanised steel and suspended by wires from the structure above. Pipes, cables, beams and other intrusive elements can thus be concealed, and the acoustic climate of a room may be improved, subject to a large number of other environmental factors.

Suspended ceiling systems can be very expensive, but because they create a void above the room in which services can be carried, they provide flexibility for planning layouts. They are particularly useful for larger open-plan offices, but where a demountable partitioning system is required the ceiling system must be designed to provide suitable fixings at regular intervals. Some manufacturers offer combined ceiling and partitioning systems that comprise a complete co-ordinated modular wall, ceiling, lighting and service outlet system, with service points above floor level.

Apart from purely functional considerations, the treatment of a ceiling can give even the smallest space a special interest through the use of colour, pattern and texture, or perhaps by variations in height.

Various alternatives to the normally unbroken plane of a suspended ceiling are available, especially for fully open-planned offices. This system consists of a suspended grid of sound absorbent sheets 250mm deep made from compressed mineral wool with aluminium connectors. Such a system permits lighting and other service outlets to be situated above the grid with comparatively easy access for maintenance.

Awkwardly shaped or very high ceilings are a special challenge. Ceilings need not necessarily be an unbroken horizontal plane; they can consist of slabs or grids of wood, metal or other suitable material, with lighting fittings deeply recessed. In such cases the fire resistance of the construction must be carefully checked with the authorities beforehand.

Walls and partitioning

Walls are even more important, both visually and functionally, than floors and ceilings, although their effect declines in very large office spaces. In a smaller office their surface treatment can give an impression of size or bulk, or provide a sense of space and continuity if they are light in colour. Solid brick or masonry walls may very well need some sort of *trompe l'oeil* treatment in a small office, and the use of a full-length mirror, curtains, or apparently open wooden slats on their surface is certainly justified if it is practicable and can be afforded.

Inevitably, the economics of change and flexibility of use have led to the frequent adoption of 'instant' walling in the shape of factory-made demountable partitions, even in the smaller office. There are currently over 80 different demountable modular partitioning systems on the

market, 75 per cent of which are metal and 25 per cent are wood framed. Some idea of comparative cost may be gained from the fact that good quality metal partitioning costs about two or three times as much as a plastered concrete block wall. The latter will have roughly twice the sound attenuation effect of the demountable partition and, within limits, can accommodate most service runs within its thickness. However, the block wall cannot be taken down without noise and dust, nor re-erected quickly – and it cannot be built on top of a carpet. Demountable office partitioning is a most valuable component in the modern office provided that its full potential and shortcomings are realised. It should be checked for:

1. Cost, for actual (not nominal) height.
2. Dimensions of standard panels width and height and whether odd spaces can be filled effectively.
3. The erection system, whether panel to panel or post/panel/post.
4. Ease of erection and demountability.
5. Sound attenuation level claimed or guaranteed.
6. Fire resistance.
7. Surface finishes and standards of details such as door furniture etc.
8. Method of accommodating services.

Sound reduction requires particular attention. Airborne sound travels through even the smallest aperture, and the effectiveness of a partition in reducing sound transmission will depend primarily on the degree to which gaps and holes can be eliminated or filled during erection. Sometimes partitions are blamed for not being soundproof when in fact the sound travels from one room to another through the void above a suspended ceiling. In this case a baffle must be inserted in the void above the partition. Fire resistance is also worth checking, and the Fire Officer will normally require a formal certificate of fire resistance where this is important. Many demountable partitions are advertised as 'incombustible', which is not quite the same thing as stating that they have, for example, a 30 minute fire resistance. Here too, fire resistant construction *must* be extended up immediately above the partition through the void above a suspended ceiling.

The need for the co-ordination of partitioning and ceiling construction has already been mentioned. Modular partitioning must also relate to the structure of a building, its windows and any built-in services. If these are ignored, junctions between partitions and columns or window mullions may be quite unsatisfactory. Window mullions – particularly those taking opening casements – may not be wide enough to accommodate a junction with the partition. If under-cill radiators interfere with the junction of the partition and an

These pictures show two of the very many demountable partitioning systems available. That at the top employs an anodised aluminium framework with composite infill panels faced in vinyl or with full glazing (as shown). That below is built up from flush-faced stove enamelled steel panels. A variety of arrangements are possible within the modular dimensions of the system chosen. The ultimate choice may very well depend on the fire resistance of the system.

outside wall, very little can be done to avoid a rather nasty junction apart from dismantling the radiator and replacing it with two smaller ones, one each side. The effectiveness of the partition as a sound barrier will depend very considerably on points such as these.

Wall and ceiling finishes
The choice of wall and ceiling finishes is almost endless, provided that any restrictions on resistance to flame spread can be met. Finishes include paints, wallpapers, fabrics, plastics, leather, cork, timber and tiling. All these have functional or decorative advantages in certain circumstances, although too many different finishes in an area can bring about visual indigestion. Practicality, with a few variations in materials or their colour and texture, is the best policy to adopt when selecting finishes for small spaces.

Textured wallpapers or vinyls are most useful for covering imperfectly finished surfaces if the texture chosen is a simple one and does not emphasise some other bad feature of the interior. Areas subjected to heavy wear should use vinyls rather than paper since the latter will quickly become dirty and worn. Vinyls may be backed with paper, fabric or foam, foam backing being a useful way of providing some thermal insulation or acoustic absorption. Many office walls will need pin-up board spaces, and these can be provided by covering insulation board panels with hessian or some other hard-wearing fabric. Alternatively, coloured and textured cork tiles are available to cover whole walls or parts of them, either for decoration or as pin-boards.

There are many flexible covering materials available, using fabrics or natural materials including grasscloth, silk and sisal. These are clearly more suitable for use in boardrooms or private offices than in heavily used areas. Timber, in the form of slats, narrow boarding or veneers, is well worth considering, especially where heavy wear resistance and decorative warmth must be combined. Not quite in the same category but also very useful as room dividers or wall and window coverings are curtains, and vertical and horizontal blinds in a variety of materials. It is very often cheaper, and certainly more attractive, to disguise old walls with a very poor surface or old windows by hanging a curtain or a blind in front of them. This is not only a useful disguise but, in the case of a wall, can be used to gain extra, hidden space.

Windows
Windows are often undervalued as part of the office scene. Their main purpose is, of course, to let light and air in while keeping the elements out. In addition, they sometimes offer an interesting view. The design of some windows, however, gives a good view out but makes it difficult to get air without producing draughts and letting rain in. Horizontal sliding windows are particularly poor in this respect. Horizontal pivoting windows are very pleasant – they provide a view, keep out rain and let in air – but they tangle with blinds or curtains unless these are hung at least 300 or 400mm away from them. Office windows that have openings on the same level as their internal cills tend to be a nuisance because no papers can be

left on the cill without the danger of their being blown in or out.

Doors
Doors in offices get very heavy use, and unless their finishes, door furniture and viewing panels are well designed and made they can very quickly begin to look scruffy. Door 'furniture' consists of handles, push and kick plates, door closers, keyhole and name plates, and so on. These should be selected from one range so that designs and materials match. Fire authorities sometimes insist on glazed viewing panels in doors of private offices to facilitate warning in case of fire. Some privacy is lost as a result, but the desk and other furniture can be positioned to minimise this. Where such a door has to be locked the panel should be of wired glass. Locks and latches need to be selected carefully. Internally the quality of locks can be related to the quality of doors, because it may be as quick for a thief to break the door open as to pick its lock. Entrance and exit doors should be of solid construction and have mortice locks with not less than seven levers. Keeping track of keys can be a nuisance in smaller offices where different members of staff work different hours. This can be overcome by having a card-operated door lock which will open only when a programmed card is inserted. If cards are lost, the cards and the lock can be reprogrammed without having to change the lock. The police can advise on appropriate security arrangements.

However commonplace the view from a window may be, it can be designed to add a further dimension to an office space.

SECTION FIVE: *furniture and fittings*

Design variety

Just as attitudes to office planning have radically changed in the past 10 years, so there has been a corresponding revolution in office furniture. Once it was difficult to find an office desk that was not as heavy and solid as a coffin, and relatively inflexible so far as linking up with other desks or equipment was concerned. Since then office furniture has adjusted and adapted so that it aids rather than hinders work, and the best designs recognise the fact that chairs, tables, cupboards and screening must be regarded as mutually dependent – a series of linked pieces of equipment like cogs in a machine. Manufacturers have been encouraged to produce a variety of designs with different characteristics and appearance, and there is a wide range of good office furniture on the market. Careful selection to suit particular space and operational needs will repay the trouble.

Physical considerations

The first important factor to watch is that of the physical dimensions of chairs, desks and tables. These basic dimensions affect the posture and ease of working of everyone, from chief executive to office junior. A British Standard (BS 3893:1965) gives a recommended range of dimensions for office desks and chairs. These are indicated in the diagram. It is, however, as well to be aware of the underlying intentions of these 'standard' dimensions. The principles behind them were described in two earlier British Standards (BS 3044:1958 and BS 3079:1959) and, as summarised below, they make a useful checklist.

CHAIRS

1   Seats should not be higher than the length of the lower leg plus heel (430mm suits most people). For office machine operators seat height should be adjustable.

2   Seats should be slightly less deep from back to front than the distance from the sitter's back to the back of the calf when seated (380mm maximum; 330mm minimum) and should be padded.

3   The seat should not be too narrow (406mm minimum).

4   The seat may slope downwards towards the back at an angle of about 3°.

5   The arms, if any, should not be too close together (480mm minimum) between the insides and of 40mm minimum width.

LEFT *This typist's chair is designed quite deliberately with a non-adjustable backrest which should provide proper lumbar support for normal adults. Although the seat height is adjustable, the manufacturer believes that unnecessary adjusting mechanism can actually encourage users to adopt incorrect positions. Be that as it may, the model here amply illustrates the correct posture.*

OPPOSITE *The range of adjustment available in chair seat height and backrest position is of major importance and staff should be instructed in how to alter these to obtain the best working position. Almost all British office furniture sizes are based on the recommendations of BS 3893:1965. The BS recommended size for a clerical desk for use with A4 stationery is shown opposite, top right. For comparison, the desk top on the left is deeper and narrower and was derived from a Swedish standard concerned with relating desk space to paper sizes.*

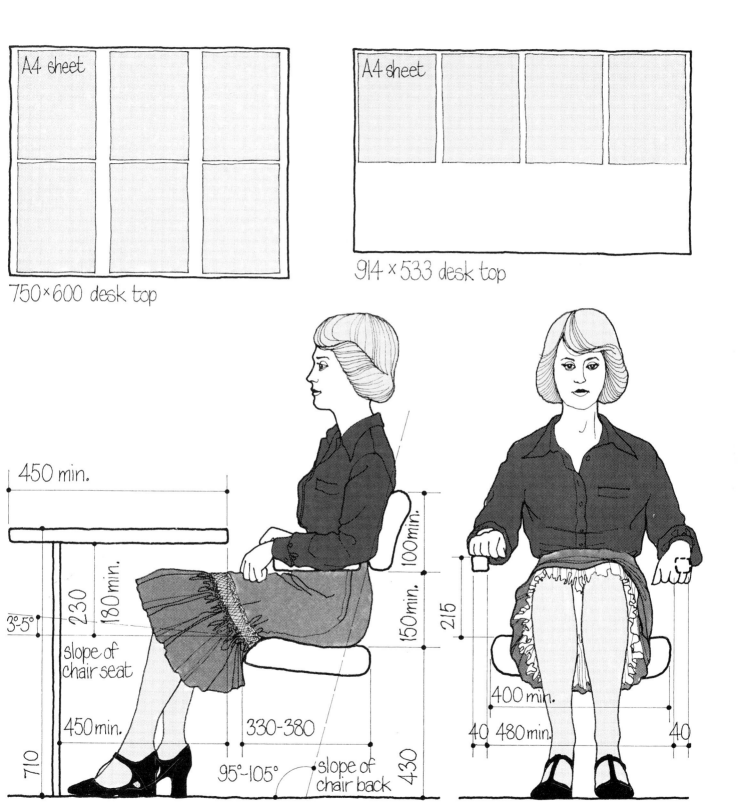

A4 sheet

750×600 desk top

A4 sheet

914 × 533 desk top

450 min.

3°–5°

slope of
chair seat

230

180 min.

450 min.

710

330–380

95°–105°

slope of
chair back

100 min.

150 min.

430

215

400 min.

40 480 min. 40

LEFT *For those who prefer their seating to be plain and simple, this straightforward chair framed in beech provides one answer.*

BELOW *This clutch of chairs for secretarial and clerical use is from only one manufacturer's range, but it illustrates the diversity of shapes and forms available on a standard base. With a hundred chairs of this kind on the market it pays the buyer to be critically discerning before making a purchase.*

6 The arms must be high enough to be useful, but not so high as to cause hunching of the shoulders (215mm from a compressed seat recommended).

7 The back rest should be curved both from top to bottom and from side to side and it should be fairly long, sloping backwards at an angle of 95 to 105° or adjustable. It should also be shaped to allow the buttocks to project backwards beyond the effective depth of the seat and should be padded.

8 Short, bar-shaped back rests should be at least 100 to 125mm deep. The lower edge should not be more than 156mm above the seat to avoid catching the shoulder blade.

9 The back rest must support the lumbar region (the lower part of the back). It is better if it is long enough also to support the thoracic region (upper middle part) and if it is curved back so as not to catch the shoulder blades.

10 The back rest should not be so wide as to interfere with the elbows.

If executive chairs are a matter of personal choice, the sitter has a wide range to choose from, not only in terms of appearance and construction, but also in mechanism. Those shown below can be ordered to include height adjustment, swivelling, tilting, automatic return after swivelling, on a pedestal or slider base and with or without castors. That on the left is constructed of a double shell of polypropylene with PVC edge trim, foam padding and a polished chrome base. The chairs on the right are wood framed with steel zig-zag sprung seats and elastic webbed backs with rubber cushions, cast aluminium arms and chrome bases.

This typist is sitting on a well designed adjustable chair and at a desk top which is also adjustable in height. Neither has been adjusted to suit her, or the kind of work she is doing, and over a period of time she is likely to suffer general fatigue, backache and a lowering of productivity.

Timber framed desk/tables with mobile pedestal storage units form part of a good-looking executive range of office furniture. The timber can be in either white ash or dark brown lacquer, with bronze anodised aluminium drawer pulls.

DESKS

1 The desk top must not be so high as to cause hunching of the shoulders (710mm is recommended).
2 The desk must not be too narrow (450mm absolute minimum) but obviously depends on purpose.
3 The underside of the desk must be high enough to give adequate knee clearance (vertical clearance above a seat should be 230mm, which means a kneehole space height of 660mm and a desk top thickness of 50mm, making a deep cross bar or kneehole drawer impracticable).
4 The minimum kneehole width should be 585mm.

These dimensions are, of course, intended as a guide, and some work functions do not allow their strict adoption. For instance, if a typewriter desk surface is 50mm lower than the adjoining desk, the kneehole space below it will be reduced to about 200mm rather than the recommended 230mm.

Flexible screening/desk support systems are altered simply and easily to provide fully enclosed, semi-enclosed or work group spaces as required. They offer an acceptable compromise between fully enclosed and totally open offices. Their effect on the environment standards of the office should be very carefully considered. Lighting, heating and ventilation do not always have the same flexibility of operation as the screening systems.

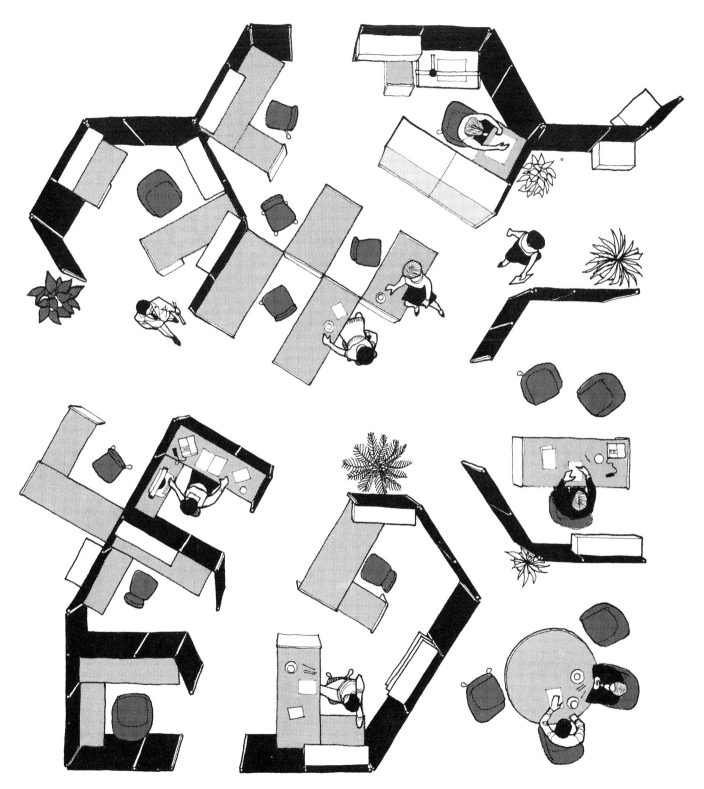

73

Selection

Selecting furniture for the smaller office needs special care and thought because of the great effect it will have on efficiency and morale. Selection on the basis of a single set of criteria may be misleading; what is wanted is a detailed look at the needs of each individual, their movements, storage needs, and the hour to hour use to which their desk is put. This does not mean that every person must have a tailor-made desk or chair, but it does mean that a sweeping decision to equip an entire office using a single range from the most recently arrived catalogue or salesman can be a mistake. On occasions it does pay a small office in rather restricted space to have specially built desk units tailored to suit their work needs. The extra cost of doing so must then be weighed against the period over which such units will be used and other factors, such as flexibility. Separate items of furniture should not be selected independently, because each is complementary in function. A market survey can be made in various ways, but sources of information include the Design Council's Design Index, the British Furniture Manufacturers Federation (who have a list of office furniture manufacturers), office equipment magazines and, of course, showrooms where equipment is displayed.

Chair range

A survey of chairs for office use will reveal a bewildering array of shapes, sizes and materials, and a wide range of price. At the time of writing, there are well over 200 different models of executive or managerial chairs on the market, and about 100 different typist/secretarial chairs. Prices for the former range from well over £200 down to £30, and for the latter from £50 down to about £12. Almost half the executive chairs are now steel framed, with most of the rest in wood and a few in aluminium. General office chairs are also predominantly steel framed for strength. Wooden chairs are not always robust enough for general use in an office. The great majority of executive chairs have swivel and tilt action and they can be upholstered in hide, fabric, or synthetic coverings. Few general office chairs have tilt action, but most swivel and have adjustable seat and backrest height. They are normally available in fabric or synthetic covering materials only.

Most manufacturers offer designs that meet the BS recommendations, but a number of other points should also be considered. For the general office, adjustable seat height will get over the problem of fitting chairs to different people, but the mechanism employed must be strong and easily adjusted.

It is worth showing staff how to adjust the chair to suit them – that is by sitting on the chair, putting their hands under thighs and then adjusting the chair until their feet just touch the floor. One good reason for getting the height right, apart from posture, is that upholstery and clothing can otherwise wear very unevenly. Whether chairs should have plastic slides, castors or wheels depends on the task and the floor covering. Wheels can be a disadvantage on smooth floors and sliders generally wear the toughest carpet.

Chair adjustment, size and bulk

A swivel mechanism is very useful where space is limited, since it enables easier access to desks. A tilting mechanism is pleasant but not essential; it allows the sitter to stretch out and straighten his or her knees, which is mainly a psychological relief. Arms on a chair can sometimes prevent the user from sitting close enough to the desk, unless he or she has a particularly long thigh measurement, so that the back support is of little use. In fact, chairs with arms are of doubtful value for general clerical use, although they do provide support when the sitter is leaning back in the chair for long periods, as in a meeting room.

The weight of chairs is also important. It may not be a problem with general office chairs, but executive and boardroom chairs, which may have to be moved around from time to time, are often made to appear deliberately heavy and bulky in an attempt to look impressive – a prime example of thoughtless design. Weight is, in fact, too rarely mentioned in manufacturers' catalogues. Stability is another important factor, but chair bases should relate to the sort of use the chair will get, and the current enthusiasm for an elaborate five-star base does look out of place on chairs of otherwise slight construction. Bases of this type are not really necessary except on large cumbersome chairs and add unnecessarily to the cost.

Upholstery

Chair upholstery suffers heavy wear, particularly in a general office, and replacement is often difficult or

Part of a range of desks, chairs and storage units designed to facilitate maximum utilisation of a work area. The shaped desks link together easily because of their shape and are made of moulded polyurethane foam on a steel frame. They are virtually scratch proof and permit two working heights, 720 and 660mm.

impossible. Some general office chairs have removable covers over a foam rubber base and these are easily replaced without sending the chair away. Not enough thought has been given to this simple problem by manufacturers. Special mention should be given to the various chairs moulded in polypropylene, which offer very good, durable value for money for general use, although normally without adjustments and with minimal upholstery. It is a pity, however, that the shapes available are not more imaginative in their use of the material.

Flexibility of layout

Desks have developed in several interesting ways to meet the demand for flexible use, particularly in open-plan offices. Here free-standing screening is often used, linked to, or partially supporting, desks and storage furniture, or simply to define working areas around groups of desks.

Such systems are increasingly becoming regarded as an essential adjunct to desk furniture, with complex desk layouts related to screening systems. The question of the operational effectiveness of such layouts, particularly in large, so-called open-plan layouts, is a matter for O & M experts to comment on, but

certainly they can be altered easily, and are flexible in use.

The systems themselves are often good-looking and ingenious. Most of them accommodate cables and wires internally and some allow lights, telephones and power sockets to be clipped on. Some manufacturers have built up entire office systems linking work surfaces, storage units, shelving and so on with screening on a modular basis, but their haphazard use can be both operationally and visually disastrous. Planned intelligently, however, they can provide a well designed and co-ordinated environment.

Co-ordination of furniture

Screen-linked furniture is as yet only a small proportion of the enormous range of desk and work-top furniture available. There are currently some 350 executive desks and over 150 clerical and secretarial type desks are available at prices ranging from about £800 down to £50. Many of these are built up from standard components to suit particular needs, with a number of different work-top sizes supported on wooden or metal frames or 'pedestal' storage units. If a frame is used then the storage units may be suspended beneath the work-top – sometimes with a clear space beneath them to the floor. The stability of frames depends on the rigidity of their connection to the work-top. It is worth remembering that a heavy, moving carriage typewriter, for example, can be a severe load on a lightly framed work-top, and it will loosen joints and fastenings in a very short time. Desks for typists must therefore be as strong and rigid as possible.

Some manufacturers supply link pieces that enable desks and tables to be joined up in different ways, including 45° and 60° angles. Most secretarial desks can have an extension typing unit attached at 90°, usually 50mm below desk top height. Retractable typewriter platforms are useful only where typing is very much a secondary activity. Desk tops can be finished in various materials, including wood veneer, lino and melamine, but shiny reflective tops should be avoided (see Section Three). Desk storage systems vary considerably and are worthy of close examination. There are many ingenious and space saving devices here, including movable stationery dividers, filing systems, sliding trays and so on. Female employees will welcome a lockable space for handbags and spare shoes. As an addition, a mobile pedestal storage unit can be sited conveniently close to the desk where the work demands it or where people prefer a simple 'table-type' work-top without units beneath it. This will obviously limit the amount of material that can be stored close at hand, and for those who need a great

An enclosed, clearly defined work area has been created here by using a combination of standard storage units and matching, screened work station units. The work station consists of 1400×750mm PVC covered worktops set within white melamine covered screens 1320mm high. All units have wiring ducts for electrical and telephone services, and a variety of co-ordinated storage, lighting, pinboard and other fittings can be incorporated. The chairs shown are available in either adjustable or non-adjustable form.

amount, a fairly large desk and an L-shaped side extension will be necessary. Section or master storage units are really useful, even in smaller offices, since they can serve the needs of an entire work group, often more efficiently than the traditional four-drawer type of cabinet.

Executive furniture

Status symbolism and fantasy often play a part in the selection of executive desks and furniture, and professional style is certainly a factor that should be considered. However, it is remarkable how often the most elaborate (and very frequently most expensive) designs begin to look outdated in a very short space of time. Fortunately there are many well designed executive desks on the market that combine good looks with efficient function. These desks usually form part of a range of furniture that includes meeting tables, storage cabinets, bookshelves and so on and, if it can be afforded, co-ordination of these elements is a good idea. As with other furniture, matching colour with the rest of the interior will contribute to an impression of order. Timber finishes

Continuous, linked work surfaces can be shared by several people. These two examples both employ a triangular unit to link standard ranges of desks and storage units at three or four different angles and at three or four different heights, depending on function. The one at the top has an oak veneered worktop supported on a steel framework or on veneered storage units. The other example has a hardwood veneer top supported on veneered or polyurethane finished storage units.

This system is based on a modular grid, and its basic components are a series of panel-hung, wall-hung and free-standing desk, storage and other units. These combine with a range of aluminium posts and screen panels which can be curved, straight or glazed in three different heights and various widths to form individual work areas of more or less privacy, as required.

can be sympathetically matched by colour and grain, if not exactly by species, and work surfaces should harmonise with other colours in the room.

The function of executive desks and tables also needs careful consideration. The area of work surface may need to be large in order to accommodate large numbers of papers and files, but this can be provided by having a main desk and an L-shaped work-top. Even so, the main desk may look formidably large, and some manufacturers try to reduce this effect by using two materials on the work surface. Where small meetings are often held, a separate small conference table may be needed. Alternatively, desk-tops that project well beyond their supporting structure allow a meeting to take place round them – a useful point where space is limited. Where there is no such restriction, a more relaxed meeting or discussion space can be obtained by providing upholstered lounge chairs around a low table, an arrangement that is becoming increasingly popular. Some firms will, of course, need a separate conference room and, depending on the numbers likely to be involved, the shape of conference table can be important, as mentioned in Section Two.

Many office furniture ranges comprise components which can be linked to provide a multitude of desk arrangements and sizes with matching side extensions, storage units and screens. The storage units can be adapted for a wide variety of uses. RIGHT *Here the desk is constructed on an enamelled steel frame with a teak veneered work surface, brown lacquered pedestals and plastics drawer pulls. The storage units are on castors for easy movement.* BELOW RIGHT *In this example, the desk frames and legs are rectangular hollow section steel or aluminium with teak or oak veneered tops. Note the adjustable shelving strips on the screens, which provide useful storage near the work surfaces.*

OPPOSITE *Part of a co-ordinated range of screen-mounted and free-standing furniture. The screens, of varying heights, can be glazed or fabric covered. They span aluminium posts and are either self supporting or are stabilised by furniture. The posts can support cantilevered desks, storage units, lighting, coathooks, shelving etc. They also provide concealed ducts for electric and telephone cables.*

Well designed storage furniture for executive areas can combine practical capacity with elegance. This example is constructed in rosewood with a stainless steel pedestal. Space-saving sliding doors disappear within the lower cabinet, which houses a small refrigerator.

A conference table is often a focal point of the office and to some extent a symbol of prestige. This example is in rosewood with chromed steel legs and is available in three different lengths in various veneers.

OPPOSITE *Modern, very high quality executive furniture of the kind illustrated here is often beautifully made and can add distinction to an otherwise mundane office interior. The desk shown is made to order, providing for a personal choice of veneer, work surface and drawer arrangements.*

SECTION SIX: *equipment and paper*

Even the smallest office can employ equipment and systems to make administration easier and more effective. These can have a decided effect on the environment of the office, a point not always appreciated by either management or designers. The mechanical and managerial criteria by which they may be judged are beyond the scope of this book, but the careful choice of equipment and systems can make an important contribution to the efficiency of an office and will certainly gain in significance as labour costs increase.

Filing systems

One of the first pieces of equipment the office will acquire is almost certainly a filing system. On this basic acquisition much will depend, for a wrong decision will prove to be expensive at a later stage. There are several basic filing methods, as follows:

1 Shelf filing, in which file covers keep the records vertically upright and hold the identification tabs. This is the simplest and most straightforward method.
2 Lateral filing systems, which are similar except that the file covers are the carriers and hang on rails within the system.
3 Vertical suspension systems, in which files are put in pockets hung from runners in desks, cabinets or trolleys. Identification tabs, and the insertion and retrieval of files, are from the top.
4 Rotary systems, in which files are suspended as in lateral filing, but radiating out from a central revolving pillar.
5 Mobile systems, which are large multi-tiered filing cabinets with vertical or lateral suspension filing cabinets with vertical or lateral suspension filing that are on floor tracks to enable access.

Detailed development of these systems has been concerned with saving space, allowing easy retrieval and giving protection to files and records, and these points must be considered in order to select the most appropriate system for the office. There is a vast range of proprietary fittings available and there should be no difficulty in finding one to suit a particular purpose.

In selecting the right system, a number of factors must be considered. Probably the most important is retrieval. Careful assessment must be made of frequency of retrieval, the degree of urgency, and who will be operating the system. The next consideration is the volume of filing involved and its rate of growth. What may be a few files this year can be a hundred or more by next year, affecting both retrieval and, eventually, the space involved.

Consideration must also be given to the relative emphasis to be placed on personal, group or centralised filing. An executive may want to keep files near his desk in a small mobile suspension unit; pleasantly designed units on castors are available for this. Alternatively, simple trolleys holding 30 to 40 suspended files give personal filing and flexibility in a small space and allow easy movement from one part of the office to another without disorder. Rotary filing is another way of ensuring easy access to about 90 to 100 files from either one person, or a small group working in close proximity. Three and four-drawer metal cabinets continue to be popular for group storage, partly no doubt because they also provide heavy and substantial screening. Their intrusion into otherwise open-plan space needs to be watched for this reason. Larger groups working together will probably require a large number of files concentrated in relatively small space. For this lateral filing cabinets are very suitable and can save up to 60 per cent of the space needed for drawer filing. Multi-tiered lateral filing not only saves space but can be easily extended: some units accommodate a mixture of lateral filing, drawer and rack storage and space for hanging artwork. Central filing in a separate area or room can have files stacked to the ceiling on shelves or suspended filing systems – providing that an absolutely safe means of

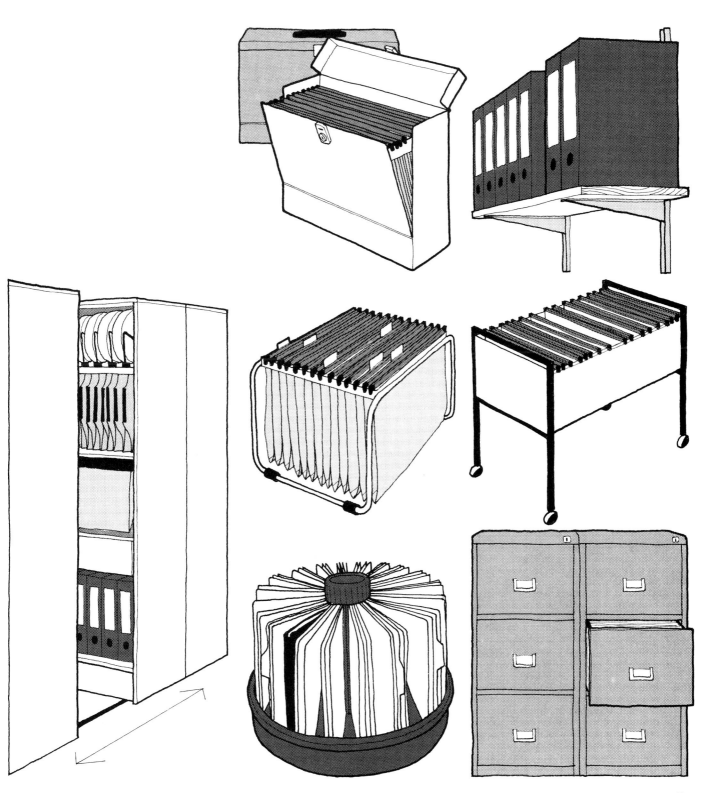

83

LEFT *Shelf filing is simple but can be a nuisance unless classification is absolutely clear. This versatile system enables shelf storage of bound books, catalogues, plain files or wallets in three different ways, in special containers, in a suspension or between moveable dividers, none of which can be accidentally displaced. The system is built up from a number of interlocking units, along an entire wall if necessary.*

BELOW *This mobile filing is moved on concealed wheels along special floor tracks either forwards and backwards or from side to side. In the latter case the back row of cabinets can remain fixed. Doors, if required, need only be placed on the front fittings. This is a good way of concentrating storage or filing for day-to-day or medium-term use. Internal arrangements may be adjusted to suit special needs.*

access is available to retrieve files at the higher levels. Mobile units allow even greater concentration of central filing and are used primarily for long-term, or archival, storage. This results in considerable floor loading so that they need careful location. They are thus of limited value to the smaller office.

The degree of protection required for documents can vary from simply excluding dust to the need for complete security and fire protection for confidential files. Dust protection can be given by a PVC or canvas roller blind on the front of a cabinet, but greater protection will entail doors, shutters or drawers, all of which take up additional space when open. When planning a filing installation, therefore, it is important to include allowance for access space such as opening drawers or reference shelves. Very important documents should be kept in fire resistant cabinets or safes and this is particularly applicable to magnetic data storage, which should have its own special provisions for fire detection and prevention.

Microfilm
Related closely to filing in hard copy form is the application of microfilm to information storage and retrieval. Letters, documents or drawings are reduced photographically and the film, on reels or in 'fiches', can be stored in very little space, rapidly retrieved and read by means of a special viewer. It is often mistakenly thought that microfilm is only useful when space is at a premium. In fact, microfilming techniques offer considerable advantages in terms of speed and accuracy of information handling and retrieval because of their integrity – single pages cannot go missing. A single microfilmed document can (using the appropriate format) be located among thousands in less time than it would take for the user to get to the traditional filing cabinet. In addition, microfilm offers better security and, when needed, enables inexpensive mailing of large amounts of documentation.

Microfilm is utilised in a variety of formats and sizes: it can be produced as roll film, cassettes, cartridge, microfiche, jacket fiche or on aperture card in 16mm or 35mm. Of these, the last three deserve explanation: essentially they refer to methods of storing film in a flat

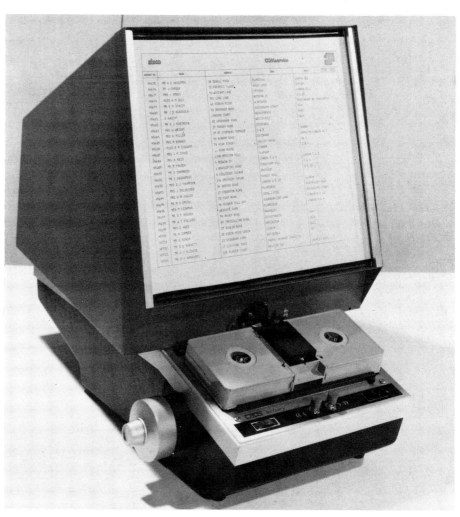

This microfilm reader is simply controlled by two buttons for forward or reverse winding. Microfilmed documents can be scanned quickly and identified on the screen. Such a system enables easy day-to-day reference to office correspondence, sales figures, bought ledgers and so on without having to retrieve the original documents, and microfilm systems can save valuable space in a small office.

format with three different densities of packing ('fiche' becomes comprehensible if thought of as a film 'mount'). Aperture cards comprise cards (about 180×75mm) upon which *one* microfilm is mounted. These are very suitable for the reduction of drawings and illustrations especially on 35mm film. Jacket fiche comprises several separate *strips* of film usually mounted on a postcard-size sheet, normally accommodating about 60 to 70 16mm frames in one sheet. Microfiche comprises one postcard-sized sheet of film on which have been photoreduced about 100 documents in 16mm frames. Microfiche is more suitable for routine correspondence than for special documents such as drawings because it is impossible to update any one individual item on the fiche without an entirely new microfiche being produced. All these methods may be coded for easy, quick retrieval: in the case of jacket fiche and aperture card by means of a simple punch card system.

To get the full benefit of a microfilm system the office must obviously establish its objectives followed by a careful appraisal of potential equipment. To put documentation or other material on film there are a variety of camera systems ranging from a basic one-off camera, which looks and operates just like a conventional office copier, up to high-speed systems which automatically apply a coding signal for subsequent retrieval. A small total system consisting of camera reader and reader/printer suitable for all microfilming save microfiche, could be acquired for about £2000 not counting film costs. At the other extreme, where a large volume of paperwork is being dealt with, as for instance with an insurance broker or a credit checking organisation, a high-speed system with digit coding for each document may be indicated, the total system costing up to say £5000. All these microfilming processing methods may be operated relatively simply by clerical staff with no specialist training.

These capital costs are high and may scare those who might otherwise wish to explore this field. The budget way of using microfilm is therefore to get the filming process undertaken at modest cost by a specialist agent. For quick reference purposes the office may then need a microfilm reader, the minimum cost of which will be about £150. But if enlargement of a document is often necessary, a reader printer will be required to enlarge and print it back from microfilm to hard copy form. The cost of this will be from about £1500. Of course, a reader can also be hired and enlargement and printing obtained from a specialist.

Safes

Some offices, even small ones, will need the special security of a safe. Small-capacity safes can be removed to be cracked open at leisure, so it is advisable to use a built-in or floor safe, of which there are several available. Safes can be obtained that are resistant to almost any hazard – including fire, explosives and drilling. Capacities vary from about 1600cc up to 245,000cc. Weight is clearly an important factor; free-standing safes vary between 400 and 2000kg, so a special floor loading capacity may be needed for some of them, either by strengthening existing floors or by designing certain areas to take such loadings.

Typewriters

The typewriter is still the most ubiquitous piece of mechanical equipment in the office. A big range is available: about a dozen manufacturers market some 70 electric models, and about the same number of manual ones. Typefaces, spacing and so on vary for different purposes, with carriage lengths variable to suit different widths and types of paper. Typewriters create noise and vibration, take up desk space, require physical effort to use, and, finally, need a power supply if they are electric. The noise produced varies, but since it comes from the type striking the paper on the typewriter platen, it can never be completely eliminated. If noise has been eliminated by the adoption of a 'soft touch', then it is probable that carbons will be difficult to read. Typewriters without a moving carriage – the 'golfball' type – take up less desk space than other models, and typefaces can be changed easily by substituting another golfball head. Electric machines in general are less tiring to use, and give absolutely even printing regardless of the skill of the typist. In fact, the expenditure of effort required to shift a manual carriage return, the associated noise and possibility of uneven typing, makes the purchase of manual typewriters a doubtful proposition except where budgets are tight. Even then, leasing of electric typewriters is possible: increased productivity will thereby help to cover the rental. Ideally, a typewriter should be tried

It takes about four hours for a typist to learn how to use a word processor of this type and a futher two days to exploit its potential to the full. The keyboard is similar to that of a normal typewriter, but with additional 'function' keys. The machine allows an operator to enter text on a visual display unit while at the same time storing the information electronically.

When the typist is satisfied with the end result the high-speed electronic printer within the machine can be instructed to type out the final corrected text. Later amendments are also facilitated. Texts are stored on magnetic cards or floppy discs, the latter being capable of storing up to 128 pages of typing.

out by a really proficient typist on the desk and in the room where it is going to be used before buying. Weights vary considerably, from 21 up to 28kg, and the amount of vibration they produce varies accordingly. The desk itself may resonate, and this can be reduced by supporting the machine on a thick insulating felt or rubber pad. Trailing cables for electric machines must be avoided, so proper planning of services is essential.

Word processing

Good typists often point out that a good quality electric machine will result in the production of more and better work each day than is likely with the manual machine. If the amount of text being handled is minimal and restricted to a few letters this may be true, but if the volume of typing is growing and there is pressure both of time and staff, the office may well be ready for the adoption of automated typing and 'word processing'. 'Word processing' essentially comprises a typewriter connected to a memory system, which consisted originally of magnetic tape, but more recently has become magnetic card. This development was inspired by the fact that a major part of a typist's time was proved to be spent either correcting mistakes, or going slowly in order to avoid mistakes. By recording typing key strokes on a magnetic card, the typist is enabled to go as fast as possible, at draft speed, to the end of the letter or report. It is then replayed from the magnetic tape, obvious errors simply corrected, and a finally corrected output obtained within seconds. The productivity gains are

significant: it is claimed that 100 per cent increase in typing loads are possible or a 50 per cent decrease in typing staff. Significantly for the smaller office, it has been suggested that the break-even point for a small business is seven letters per typist per day.

Word processing technology has moved fast and it is now possible for a typist to face a video screen on which the text appears as the electronic keyboard is operated. For the smaller office making its first venture into automated typing, the 'stand alone' word processor is likely to be the best choice.

It is both simple to operate and has the scope to handle a wide range of tasks such as mailings and reports in addition to normal correspondence. It comprises a typewriter keyboard and memory unit as part of one integral unit about the size of a two-drawer filing cabinet and 'standing alone'. It can cost in the region of £2000 and the training of the operator takes three or four days plus practical experience using the machine. Productivity gains of the order of 200 per cent are claimed from diligent typists so that, with typists' salaries in London averaging £3000 per annum, the initial outlay could be recovered fairly quickly where large amounts of routine typing are involved.

Dictating machines

Of all the equipment in the office, an efficiently used dictating system gives the quickest and best return on its investment. It has often been proved that shorthand dictation is one of the most expensive ways of getting words onto paper because of

the uneconomic utilisation of time by both dictator and typist. The first essential therefore is the employment of two machines: one for dictation and the other for transcribing. While dictating is taking place the typist can be getting on with other work; if the dictation is interrupted no one is kept waiting. There are added benefits in that dictation from several people can be dealt with by one typist, and that dictation carried out late in the day can be ready for transcription in the morning. More than 75 types and sizes of dictating machines are available, from the miniature 'memo-taker' to equipment suitable for recording conference proceedings. The recording medium can be either non-magnetic plastic belt or disc, or magnetic belt, disc tape, wire or film, and machines can be desk-top or portable.

The typist doing transcription work will find it very annoying to have to cope with other tasks, such as answering telephones, and, to be efficient, should be exclusively employed for audio-typing. The transcription desk must be large enough to take a typewriter, the dictating machine and accessories. Dictation and playback can be a disturbance in, or disturbed by, a small open office. If there are more than six potential users, it may be worth considering having a centralised dictating pool. This implies having several typists transcribing dictation full-time from all letter writers and is, in fact, the most cost-effective system where a large volume of outgoing correspondence or reports are involved. The alternative is the group system which channels all dictation work into a common recording bank for transcription by one or two typists. Compatible pocket note-taking recorders can also be used as part of such a system by people such as sales staff, surveyors and so on, who work away from the office: the recording medium – for instance tape cassettes – can be easily sent through the post for transcribing.

Calculators and computers

Various programmable electronic calculators are now familiar in the smaller office. The calculator has gone through a series of rapid changes since the first machines appeared. The first were large desk-top machines and development has reduced these down to the current popular hand-held, wallet-thin models. Emphasis has also been placed on an increased ability to cope with bigger information loads so that now pocket machines are available that can be programmed, attached to printers and, in one instance, communicate with the user through plain English printed words. These machines are immeasurably valuable in the handling of accounts and other calculations required by the smaller office and are often an interim step to the small desk-top computer. This is because calculators at present available still require considerable

labour in sorting and identifying sums and quantities related to different purposes. Large volumes of figures and the calculations and data relating to those figures can be handled with great speed and accuracy by a small computer operated by only one person.

The first small computers were a development from the mechanised manual accounting system where records were kept on magnetic stripe visible record cards ('VRC'). The cards held the details in both written form and magnetic form on the

stripe. The current equivalent is a mini-computer which takes up less space than an office desk and uses the so-called 'floppy disc' to store information. These discs are about the size of a 45rpm gramophone record and are tough enough to be handled, sent through the post and so on, without damage.

The smallest system can typically carry data on, say, 1000 customers and 3000 stock items; by adding further data recording discs this can be increased to 3000 customers and 10,000 stock items.

This compact small business computer system uses a low-cost 'diskette' to store information. High-speed input and output enable data to be stored off-line or transmitted by post. The diskette can also be used to store key business files or historic information for security purposes. Up to 2000 records are available to the operator within one minute of placing the diskette in the system.

Standard programmes are available (though special ones can be made) to cover the compilation of payrolls, bought and nominal ledgers, and general account ledgers, sales and stock accounting, stock recording, monthly sales and so on. Word processing is also possible on these machines. Average cost of mini-computers is in the region of £12,500 and currently smaller office users of them range from accountants through to machinery importers/distributors – wherever in fact there is a high volume of turnover combined with small staff and lots of paperwork.

Copiers and print machines

The copier has gone through a number of refinements over the years and now most offices are likely to have one of two basic types, both electrostatic in operation.

Until the mid-1970s, the more familiar copying machine was likely to be that employing the direct electrostatic process in which the image was formed directly on the

This microcomputer costs under £400 and uses an ordinary cassette recorder to store data. It would be suitable for the limited data processing needs of many small businesses. It consists of a 53-key input unit and microcomputer with a computer controlled recorder and a 12-inch video display monitor. Possible application include general ledger accounting, payroll, inventory control and other clerical functions.

surface of a coated paper; this surface was usually a conductive zinc oxide. The alternative was the indirect electrostatic process which formed the image on an intermediate surface and transferred it to plain paper. This latter technique was characterised by the Xerox copying system, only now being rivalled by a number of other plain paper systems. The cost per copy of the direct electrostatic system is controlled by the cost of the special paper, while the cost per copy of the indirect system is basically related to the capital cost of the copier. Other processes of copying include the dual spectrum method whereby an intermediate conveys the image to the copy paper by means of heat and pressure. It involves no powders or liquids, is entirely dry and is very suitable for smaller office needs.

Copying and printing machines and systems have proliferated: more than 150 types were on the market in 1977, varying in cost from about £8000 down to £60; the latter based on thermally sensitive paper and very suitable for home use. In selecting the most appropriate machine very careful consideration should be given to the volume of copies likely to be required per month because this factor has the greatest effect on the cost per copy. It would be fair to say, in terms of quality, that most modern machines are competitive in cost; the more significant variations to be considered being in speed of first copy production, the size of original able to be handled, the possibility of reduction or the addition of a sorter. Colour copiers are not yet widely available for purchase on the open market and it is doubtful, even if

they were, whether they would be commercially viable except in special circumstances; as a rough guide, the price per coloured A4 copy is about 50p for a minimum of five. It is particularly difficult to control copying costs since so often the equipment is used by a variety of people and often for purposes for which the copier was not designed; such as one-off copies on a volume machine, or long runs on a small desk-top copier. Size of machine does not depend on size of office and very often copiers are abused, or

Copiers are now very widely used in offices and are available in a wide range of sizes, according to the volume of work required. This model is either stream-fed or flat bed and works on the indirect electrostatic principle, copying onto plain paper. It can also cope with less usual work, including plate-making, overhead projection transparency making and addressing.

damned as inefficient or expensive, when in fact they have been wrongly chosen for the job.

There are two main categories of machine – flat bed and rotary. Flat bed machines can copy from books and magazines, whereas rotary models can only handle single sheets. Sizes and weights vary very widely, and thought must be given to their position in the office, not least because of the considerable quantity of paper and other supplies that must be stored near them. In principle, the larger the machine, the more continuous and disturbing the noise it produces, so a separate room for big machines is often advisable. Some special thermally sensitive copying paper (used in electrostatic machines) must be stored away from heat. Rotary machines for printing drawings from prepared negatives generally use the diazo, or dyeline, process, which uses ammonia vapour or liquid to develop the exposed image. Machines using ammonia sometimes require ducting to the outside of the building, which can limit their location.

It could repay the smaller office to study the viability of other reprographic systems, such as stencil duplicating and small offset litho machines. Until recently, stencil duplicating was often dismissed as inconvenient and unreliable, but the development of low-cost electronic stencil cutters now enables the stencil duplicator to rival other short-run systems. Small offset litho processing now has the benefit of electrostatic direct platemaking to give it short-run viability which, with simple sequential controls, means that little

skill is required to achieve good results.

Correspondence and stationery

It is surprising how often the time and money spent in producing a top quality letter is wasted because there are no stamps to send it off! The test of handling correspondence is not really complete until the letters are actually in the post, and to this end a franking machine, complemented by a set of accurate postal scales, can be most useful. At one time the most unpopular job in the office was carrying the franking machine to the post office for refilling. Present-day machines need only the adjustment of a small component; or the insertion of a franking card.

Just as office planning, servicing and equipment should be compatible, so all office paper and stationery should fit into a rational system. This system should, except for very special circumstances, be based upon the International A paper sizes. These interrelated sizes and proportions facilitate storage and can enable simple house guides to the setting out of letters, reports and pro formas to be drawn up. Envelopes too can be related to these A sizes.

Many offices permit a proliferation of different sizes, colours and printing styles for their stationery. This ignores the fact that, used intelligently, well designed stationery can positively aid work flow and paper identification. Unco-ordinated stationery design is not a fault exclusive to smaller companies: many household names neglect this aspect. Stationery design is properly the province of the specialist industrial designer – not purely for

International A sizes of paper and related envelope sizes now in common use.

aesthetic reasons, but because the layout and style of written information on letters and forms can make, mar or obscure serious intentions.

Commonplace points to watch in the design of stationery include the following:

1 Company information: is all the information required by law shown, including VAT and company registration numbers, as well as name, address, telephone and telex numbers? Is all this information placed on the paper and printed so that it can be easily read – after the letter has been clipped into a file? (some trendy letterheads have actually placed information vertically on the left hand side of the paper!) Is the information legible and easily read – without magnification?

2 Setting out: Is there a recognised, rational guide showing all secretaries and typists how to set out letters, including essential references, names, subjects and so on? Adoption of a standard setting out can speed up the reading and comprehension of letters – something which no machine can yet do.

3 Line widths: Is there space for the typist to print a reasonable line of words across the page, or is it limited by unnecessary logotypes, sales puffs or lists of directors? Short lines mean the use of more paper and the receipt of two pages when one would do is often a nuisance, quite apart from being an excessive waste.

4 Logos and symbols: are these comprehensible? Simplicity and directness always have greater impact than complex obscurity.

Logo design needs especial care: what looks impressive on the side of a furniture truck can seem ridiculous at the top of a business letter.

Very careful evaluation of all materials used in the stationery will pay dividends. Carbonless paper, while expensive, can save time – particularly in form filling. Coloured papers can speed identification (but watch the effect on copying!). Self adhesive 'window' envelopes are time savers; lightweight paper can reduce volume considerably for offices with a lot of outgoing correspondence. Finally, envelopes should be compatible in size with all other stationery and thus avoid unnecessary folding of paper.

SECTION SEVEN: *location and construction*

So far, this book has discussed the office scene entirely from within its walls, as if assuming that space was already chosen or occupied. This is not always the case so this section is intended to answer some of the questions which arise when seeking new office accommodation.

Locational pros and cons

There are often strong preconceptions about where an office should be located. Perhaps there is some overwhelming reason for choosing a specific site – as for instance where the main source of business is in a particular commercial area or community. But, except where daily person-to-person contact is essential, improved postal and telecommunication methods are making it less important for businesses to cluster together, like with like, in close proximity.

Out of city, suburban or rural locations may offer the following advantages:

1 A quieter, cleaner environment with a pleasant aspect and views.
2 Easier car parking for staff and visitors.
3 Lower rent and rates.
4 Less competition for staff, including casual workers.
5 Reduced staff turnover.
6 Better security.

But this idyllic prospect may be modified because of:

1 Poorer public transport, limiting availability of staff.
2 Lack of shopping and eating facilities in the neighbourhood.
3 More time spent in making essential visits outside the office.
4 Increased expenditure on telephone and postal services.

An estimate of the costs of all or most of these can generally be made for a particular site. Some disadvantages can also be turned to advantages. For example, lower than average rents may encourage the leasing of floor areas generous enough to afford above average working space per person and better environmental standards, both of which will help to attract the best staff. Simple catering facilities can be provided within the office so that the staff save time and money. The possible permutations are many, but they need to be listed and costed with care, and with an eye on future business levels, rates, rent, salaries and servicing costs.

Car parking

Car parking space and staff transport facilities can also considerably affect office location and communications. This factor is therefore a very important one, and deserves the earliest thought in choosing an office location. Car parking in towns and cities is generally limited and many buildings are accorded only restricted or shared parking space.

Enquiries should be made to the Planning Authority and to the police concerning the possibilities of road widening, traffic management schemes and bus lanes, all of which may affect street parking or unloading outside or near the office. Bus and train routes and their timetables also deserve examination.

Location of Offices Bureau

The Location of Offices Bureau was set up in 1963 as a Government Agency whose job it then was to encourage the decentralisation of offices away from city centres. The intention was to relieve the congestion of such centres, but since then the situation has changed. In 1977 the role of the LOB was redefined to 'promoting a better distribution of office employment in England and Wales', and, among other tasks, to 'promote office employment in inner urban areas'. For the smaller office organisation the decision on a city, suburban or rural location will be heavily influenced by an assessment of its annual outgoings. As recently as 1976 the LOB itself pointed out that the 'present difference in annual outgoings (salary and overheads) between central London and outside is £2600 for each member of staff employed'. For many reasons, one of which is increasing building costs, rents will almost certainly continue to rise regardless of location, so that this kind of differential between central and outer city locations will persist.

LOB *property register*

The LOB maintains a property register containing details of new offices for rent or sale throughout the country and typical rental levels. They also have information on sites for building, subject to planning permission and Office Development Permits. They can give information on the present and future availability of staff, on details of housing availability, local schools and amenities. In short any firm considering a move away from its present location should consult LOB, not only for the general picture, but for useful detailed advice.

Financial incentives

Another factor of interest is that, since October 1976, the Government has offered a number of financial incentives to employers who move offices to 'assisted areas' (Special Development, Development, and Intermediate areas). These incentives are operated by the Department of Industry and they comprise:

The assertive character of many late nineteenth-century commercial buildings makes them daunting and difficult to modify. This example in the heart of the City of London was built in 1871 and has been successfully turned into modern offices without detracting internally or externally from its original character. Very considerable modifications were in fact required, including air conditioning and double glazing to reduce traffic noise.

An old mill by the stream in deepest Staffordshire is about as idyllic a location as any frustrated commuter could imagine. Its conversion into offices left the fabric substantially unaltered, but more light was let in to parts of the interior by opening up space between the office floors.

1 A fixed grant of £1500 for each employee moving with his work to the assisted areas (up to a total of 50 per cent of the additional jobs created in these areas).

2 An additional grant of £1000 in Development Areas and £1500 in Special Development Areas for each job created.

3 Rent relief grants for office premises of up to 3 years in Intermediate Areas, 5 years in Development Areas and 7 years in Special Development Areas. Equivalent grants may be given where premises are purchased or built by employers.

4 Eligible projects may also qualify for loans at concessionary rates of interest or for interest relief grants towards capital expenditure other than on accommodation.

Type and condition of property

Following the decision about location will be the question of the type and condition of property to aim for in the chosen area. There are three basic options here:

1 'Off the shelf' accommodation in an existing building that has adequate environmental and technical services and therefore needs a minimum of modification.

2 Accommodation in an existing building either (a) with basic services that can be easily altered and augmented, as required or (b) that requires complete conversion and new services installed.

3 To construct new office space unilaterally, or in partnership with other businesses.

Descriptions of floor areas

A preliminary search for office space will best be made with the help of an

estate agent, who should be briefed on your requirements. These requirements will have emerged from previous work carried out by the office project co-ordinator in order to define the scope of the problem (see Section One). For this particular purpose, floor areas are defined in different ways, and it is important that the estate agent knows in which way you are defining your requirement. Two common ways of doing so are as follows:

'Net usable floor area': This is the area of floor space capable of being used for all the *work* purposes required by the particular office. It therefore excludes staircase, lifts, lavatories, ducts and structural columns. It will also exclude a corridor on the same floor level which serves an adjoining tenancy. It assumes reasonable ceiling heights and sufficient daylight to allow the space to be wholly usable without undue restriction. It is, in fact, the working area calculated in Section One of this book.

'Gross floor area': This is the area of space calculated to cover, not only net usable floor area, but also to include the area of staircase, lifts, lavatories, ducts and columns.

This late eighteenth-century London town house with brick load-bearing walls and wide-span timber floors is typical of domestic construction of the period. It was probably first used for offices in the early twentieth century and still offers pleasant, semi-domestic space, subject to the limitations of room size, fire restrictions and noise transmission. It is a pity that in this example, as is often the case, the original eighteenth-century glazing bars have been removed, probably during the nineteenth century.

In addition to these, the phrase 'gross area' of the building may be used, which may cause confusion. In fact 'gross area' refers to the total area of the building as measured to the *external* perimeter of the outside walls. While relevant to professional assessments concerning a building, it is unlikely to be applicable to the average office user.

Preliminary report on a property

The search for office space may produce several possibilities. It is then sensible to commission a preliminary report from an architect on pros and cons relative to the outline design requirements discussed in Section One. This will review the standard of the buildings or spaces offered, the quality of finishes, the level of services, and it may comment on the necessity, and statutory possibilities, of carrying out modifications to satisfy those requirements in which it is obviously deficient. It will also necessitate careful enquiry by a solicitor of the proposed terms of sale, or lease. Where a building or site is not classified for use as an office, the architect will need to approach the planning authority to assess the likelihood of obtaining permission (although the process of obtaining permission for change of use is a time consuming business and is not to be recommended unless very special reasons exist).

Feasibility studies

If the report is generally favourable to one of the propositions, then the next step should be to extend the commission into a planning feasibility study, together with a full structural survey. (It was this point

that Section Two of this book reached, having examined detailed planning requirements sufficiently to be able to provide a clear brief for such a study.) The feasibility study should examine how the planning and environmental standards specified at the outset can be achieved, at what order of cost and over what period of time. The difficulty with which the costs of, and times for, conversions can be assessed tends to vary directly with the age of the building and the extent of modifications to the fabric. In some cases, where particular problems of size or structure exist, the architect may find it necessary to go into more detail in the feasibility study in order to be more definite on these matters. For example, a decision to adopt central air-conditioning in an old building could have wide repercussions on the available space and the building's structure. Equally, incorporating a lift may raise special dimensional and constructional problems.

Structural surveys

Some leases and deeds of sale include special conditions about repairs and maintenance, or they may restrict the changes one can make to the building, and only a full constructional survey can disclose likely future problems and costs. Careful attention must also be paid to the uses to which adjoining parts of the building are put: an expensive but odoriferous restaurant nearby with ventilation problems may go a long way to explaining the extraordinarily generous terms offered by a landlord or vendor. The survey will disclose the

fundamental construction of the premises, which may affect later planning in the following ways:

1 Designed floor loadings (these could influence the siting of heavy items such as safes, photocopiers, bookstacks and bulk storage).
2 Existing walls (and sometimes floors which may need to be demolished or moved).
3 Acoustics and sound transmission (outside noise levels from traffic or adjoining tenants may need attention).
4 Fire worthiness and escape.
5 Surface finishes (renovation, if required, can be enormously expensive).
6 Mechanical and electrical servicing.
7 Plumbing and sanitation.

Types of construction

Construction techniques have developed and changed considerably since the eighteenth century and are still doing so. In general, construction methods were more consistently similar before the 1890s than since. There are, in general, three basic types of construction that are likely to be met with, and their broad effects on the office environment are given below.

Type 1: Load-bearing walls of brick or masonry with timber-framed and clad floors. This form of construction is economic and straightforward and is still commonly used, though more often for domestic than office construction. It is most commonly found in buildings prior to the late nineteenth century, sometimes in conjunction with metal framing where these are of the larger commercial variety. Walls were then built of thick brickwork or masonry without cavities, and floor spans varied from about 4 or 5m up to 10m depending on the size of timber or metal beams employed. This type of eighteenth or nineteenth-century building is perfectly well suited for office use and, if its natural limitations are recognised, can be converted to provide a pleasant working environment. Limitations imposed by the structure are as follows:

1 Room sizes are restricted by the positions of load-bearing walls. If larger spaces are required, then these walls must be demolished and the resulting openings strengthened by steel or reinforced concrete frames – which can be very costly.

2 Old timber floors can often take considerable loads, but this cannot be assumed, especially when heavy items such as safes or electric storage heaters are being installed, and an engineer's advice is essential. Such floors may also deflect or may already have deflected considerably, which can cause dimensional problems with partitioning.

3 Noise, and particularly impact or footstep noise, travels easily through timber floors unless they are treated with additional stiffening between the joists (and the spaces perhaps filled with a lightweight absorbent material such as vermiculite). Sound transmission between rooms divided by well built brick or masonry walls is, however, limited, which could be advantageous to smaller professional practices where confidentiality is required.

4 Fire worthiness and fire escape routes may very often be a problem, but it is difficult to generalise and if any alterations are envisaged, early consultations with the local fire officer and building engineer are essential. Timber-framed staircases may need added protection from fire, extra escape routes may be necessary, and doors between distinct 'compartments' of the building may have to conform to specific fire resistance standards and have special closing methods.

5 Service runs are not too difficult to run within timber-framed floors, but it is as well to remember that services in the ceiling, such as light circuits, can only be modified easily by taking up the floor (and any floor finishes) above, unless, of course, a suspended ceiling has been installed. Hot water circuits are more difficult because it may be necessary to cut through brickwork to achieve a satisfactory circulation. Also, unless pipes can be run within the floor space without cutting joists (which weakens them), they may be difficult to conceal. Vertical routing of services can also be difficult and special ducts may be needed. Installing lifts in this type of building often poses problems, primarily in terms of planning, but also because they can create vibration and noise.

On the whole, this type of construction can accept a wide variety of interior treatments. It is of course possible to end up with an interior that is starkly modern, in contrast to the outside. In this case a great deal of the original character of the building can be lost, and to eliminate all sense of the past in an old building is, in my view, something to be avoided.

Type 2: Loadbearing walls of brickwork or masonry with solid floors. Reinforced concrete floors are first met with from the 1890s onwards, but solid floors built up on shallow arches of clinker concrete date from the 1840s until the era of reinforced concrete. Walls are thick, often without cavities, and floor spans vary considerably depending on the exact form of construction, sometimes reinforced with metal joists. In the twentieth century this was often translated into clay pots with reinforced concrete ribs between, in spans of up to about 7m. In nineteenth-century construction, floors sometimes consist of shallow brick arches between steel joists and clinker concrete levelling out the floor above. The limitations of buildings of this type are similar to those of type 1, with some important exceptions, as follows:

1 Room sizes are less restricted than with timber floors, but where walls have to be demolished to provide large rooms, the openings will almost certainly have to be heavily strengthened, as described above.

2 Solid floors can generally take very heavy loads. In old warehouses and similar buildings their capacities are often in excess of modern requirements for office floor loadings.

3 Impact noise will travel quite easily through solid floors unless very resilient floor coverings are used, but otherwise sound reduction is good.

4 Fire resistance and escape standards are usually easy to

achieve, but any exposed metal joists will need protection, either with fireproof casings or, if ceiling heights permit, by an approved suspended ceiling below them.

5 A wide variety of finishes can be used on the floors because deflection, if any, is normally very slight indeed.

6 Solid floors cannot take service runs within their thickness and so surface ducts must be used, which may prove difficult to disguise. Breaking through floors of this type for vertical routings must be done with some care.

Generally buildings of this construction are solid, dependable, and, subject to arch or ceiling heights, capable of becoming very pleasant offices, when converted from warehouses and the like. The very weight of construction used in them makes them slower to warm up and cool down than the two other construction types discussed here, so that heating methods must be designed accordingly.

Type 3: reinforced concrete or structural steel framing with solid or semi-solid floors. This form of construction is common in nearly all modern multi-storey office buildings, although some small office buildings of two or three storeys may have load-bearing brick walls and solid floors.

Characteristics are as follows:

1 There are virtually no restrictions on the size of rooms within the internal perimeter of the building.

2 Floors are capable of taking loads up to the designed loadings, which include an allowance for partitions. Especially heavy equipment can sometimes be regarded as a 'distributed' load and assumed to be spread evenly over a requisite floor area (as opposed to the need for very specific locations in other forms of construction).

3 Sound reduction internally is good, although impact noise will still pass through the floor structure unless a resilient floor covering or special construction is used. Sound transmission from outside can sometimes be a problem when large windows have been used.

4 If the building has been designed for office use, there should be very few problems of fire-worthiness and escape.

5 There are practically no restrictions on surface finishes.

6 The main difficulty of this type of construction, depending on its age, is likely to be in the replacing or extending of services. Up to 20 years ago office buildings of this type were designed for central heating, but rarely for the extensive use of telephones and electric power machines, which is now common. Cable ducts, if any, tended to be run around the perimeter of each floor and special methods may be needed to bring cables to desks in the centre of the floor. Other details, including windows, sanitation and lifts, occasionally fall short of current standards and because of original tight planning are sometimes impossible to improve.

Age versus standards

From the above, it can be appreciated that, when accommodation is sought in an old building, standards must inevitably be very heavily influenced by its age and construction. So long as this influence is acknowledged at the outset, everyone will appreciate the reason why standards may vary from the ideal. A professional firm occupying a late eighteenth-century town house may have to adapt to the internal spaces of a comfortable domestic retreat built for a merchant 200 years ago. Structural or servicing modifications to achieve desirable standards in such a case would obviously be difficult and expensive. the firm would probably find it much easier to provide more equable standards on one well serviced floor of a modern speculative office block. On the other hand, they would forfeit the special character and atmosphere provided by the older building.

There are in fact always interesting possibilities in converting older commercial property. Old counting houses and warehouses, and sometimes factories, can be made into efficient and attractive offices – at a price. Provided that the internal spaces are not unreasonably restricted by beams and columns, old lifts, pipe shafts and chimneys, their suitability will be determined by the extent to which one is prepared to go to the trouble of refurbishing them. The conversion will probably take longer to realise, and will be more fraught with problems than any other course. But many small organisations have gone ahead and obtained efficient, well serviced and characterful office space as a result.

Standard speculative office blocks

A vast amount of the office space available was built primarily for speculation from the mid-1930s onwards. This is of varying standard, but it can offer useful, routine space suitable for division into smaller enclosed office rooms – 'cellular' offices. The plan of these buildings varies only slightly consisting of rectangular floors of between 12 to 15m width, with length depending on the site, but with a maximum of 30m between staircases. They are often framed buildings, usually with a row of columns down the middle. Dividing walls or partitions can split the length into suitably sized rooms opening off a central corridor. As has been said, the standards of heating, ventilation, lighting, power circuits, ducts, lifts, lavatories and so on vary considerably in such buildings. Although the more recent ones are serviced to acceptable current standards, very many need as much upgrading as buildings which are far older. Although open planning, in the simplistic term of omitting partitions, is possible in such spaces, the proportions of floors and levels of servicing are far from ideal for this purpose.

ABOVE *This canal-side warehouse typifies mid-nineteenth-century brick loadbearing wall construction with timber framed floors and sometimes cast-iron structural frame. Such buildings often pose particular problems in creating sufficiently large open-plan spaces, adequate window areas and proper fire escape routes.*

RIGHT *This building is typical of post-war, concrete framed commercial developments which were built for letting in sections. In spite of their comparative modernity, expensive refurbishment is sometimes necessary to bring them into line with present-day standards. They normally offer little potential for the larger open-planned organisation and their large windows can cause both excessive heat loss and excessive solar gain.*

Building new accommodation

Although it is a rare occurrence, some small businesses with, say, up to 20 or 30 staff, may want to explore the possibility of developing their own building. To a large extent this decision will depend on whether enough capital can be found and a loan negotiated. It can be a considerable advantage to approach the problem jointly with one or two other businesses of similar size, and this has, in fact, been done successfully in the past, mainly by professional firms. The advantages are obvious: accommodation can be designed in detail to suit the occupants; and the repayment of borrowed capital plus interest continues at a more or less constant level, as opposed to the vagaries of reviews every five or seven years in rented office space.

Speculative offices for open planning

The growing awareness of a need for good office environments has meant that more well planned and serviced office space is now being built by developers. Some of this has been designed specifically for open-plan layouts, to which lighting,

One way in which small firms can enjoy fully serviced open office space at reasonable cost is shown here. A circa 1900 multi-storey factory with steel frame and solid floors was converted into fully serviced open office spaces, any part of which could be rented complete with lighting, heating, power, telephones (including switchboard facilities), telex, and communal waiting, reception and even secretarial services. The upper picture shows the upgraded space before division. Space is simply divided up by moveable screens so that expansion and contraction can be catered for easily. Note that all services are housed in a ceiling grid, overcoming the problem of inserting them under existing floors and freeing floor space for screening systems.

ventilation, electricity supplies and ceilings have been closely tailored. Ironically, this kind of office space cannot always be easily adapted or be divided into smaller, enclosed offices. Professional advice will have to be obtained on the chances of providing even one or two individually enclosed offices in such a scheme. It is normally a waste of time looking at such accommodation unless it has been decided that the office shall be 95 per cent open planned. It is usually far too costly for a developer, however well intentioned, to provide well serviced space suitable for both open and cellular offices.

This pleasant small office building stands in a suburb of Cardiff and was specially designed for the local subsidiary of a London-based company. It provides a net useable office floor area of about 265m² (2830ft²) on the ground and first floors and a self-contained two-bedroom flat on the second floor. First class accommodation and an investment have thus been achieved at modest cost.

Professional input during a project

	INCEPTION	SCOPE	BRIEF	LOCATION	SURVEYS	FEASIBILITY
PROJECT CO-ORDINATOR	Assesses existing business operation, its accommodation, equipment and environment, and likely effect on productivity of improvements.	Consults with all concerned and assesses scope of proposals; possible costs and degree of disruption.	Defines guidelines on space and environmental standards, locations, flexibility and expansion and image. Sets cost limit/budget.	Decides areas for office location after investigation of facilities, grants and consultation with LOB.	Examines property options proposed by estate agent, possibly with architect. Decides on shortlist for more detailed investigations.	Decides on best proposition and commissions feasibility study to include cost and programme and work positions. May make ODP application in consultation with architect.
ACCOUNTANT		Checks availability of finance; effect on working capital and cash flow; tax implications; grants.				Checks cost implications derived from studies to date and further advises and assists on finance. Rechecks cash flow.
SOLICITOR	Assesses existing lease or freehold obligations.				Considers documentation of possible properties in principle and advises on implications.	Examines deeds of sale, checks covenants, easements and other restrictions. Advises client and architect of these.
ARCHITECT			Advises on design guidelines, likely quality, costs and programme and courses of action. Checks environmental brief.		Examines properties and advises on likelihood of meeting environmental brief. Liaises with surveyor on constructional survey.	Carries out study of possibilities in favoured property including order of cost and timetable etc. (RIBA normal service Stage B). May make outline planning application and assist in ODP application.
ESTATE AGENT			Advises on likely locations, rent or cost levels and looks for property that answers brief in general terms. Advises on attitude of planners to any new development.		Carries out survey as required; asks questions of vendor and may commence negotiations for purchase or lease.	Supplies survey report for inclusion in feasibility study.
SPECIALIST SERVICES	Management consultants may analyse business operation and report on possibility of improvements.					

ACQUISITION	DETAILED DESIGN	SPECIAL REQUIREMENTS	BUILDING WORKS OR IMPLEMENTATION	OCCUPATION	FINAL ACCOUNTING	
Instructs solicitor and estate agent to acquire property and arranges deposit.	Commissions detailed design. Starts consultations with Post Office or private sub-contractor on telecommunications.	Commissions special design requirements in interiors, furniture, stationery, logos etc.	Enters into contract with builder and/or others concerned advised by architect. Settles stage payments, checks budget.	Organises move to new offices.	Assesses final costs against budget. Pays for all work as certified.	PROJECT CO-ORDINATOR
					Checks final costs; assesses which works are allowable against tax. Advises on overall financial picture.	ACCOUNTANT
Carries out detailed searches; agrees lease or freehold documents with vendor's solicitors; arranges deposit; rent free periods etc.	Negotiates with landlord on modifications proposed and obtains licence for these.					SOLICITOR
	Carries out detailed design, planning and environmental studies including furniture and equipment layouts. Makes planning application. (RIBA normal service Stages C, D and E.)	Designs or co-ordinates special interior treatments and furniture.	Prepares production drawings and specifications. Obtains building regulations approval. Obtains tenders, arranges contract and programme. Supervises all works through to completion including Certificates of Payment. (RIBA normal services Stages F, G & H.)	Prepares maintenance manual. Checks defects six months after completion.	Checks final account. Issues final certificate for payment subject to architect's acceptance of all work as satisfactory.	ARCHITECT
Negotiates as necessary with vendor; finalises and agrees measurements of areas.						ESTATE AGENT
	Post Office advises on telecommunications and proposes options.	Interior design proposals by architect or industrial designer; other special requirements designed as required.	Production drawings of special requirements; installation of telecommunications.			SPECIALIST SERVICES

SECTION EIGHT: *professional advice and legislation*

The importance of professional advice

This book is a guide, not a manual. It has attempted to describe some of the criteria by which the design of elements in the office environment may be selected, but it has necessarily done so superficially. Properly qualified professional advice should be sought at those junctures when the scope of a problem falls outside the expertise of the management. A guide to this is given on the previous two pages. The skill of management is, as was indicated in Section One, in project co-ordination. It is therefore unwise for the co-ordinator to attempt professional tasks for which he is not trained, because he will thereby almost certainly abdicate his own vital role.

There is, in fact, considerable skill in being able to employ professional advice effectively and economically. Part of this consists of knowing when to bring in the professional and to ensure co-ordination between different professionals in a way which ensures positive progress of a project towards fulfilment. It is comparable perhaps to conducting an orchestra of highly skilled instrumentalists: the right tempo, introductions and movements must be controlled, even though the conductor has no instrument himself. In examining and progressing a project, the office will almost certainly have to consult an accountant, or a solicitor, or an architect, or an estate agent and perhaps an interior designer depending on size and intent. As to the fees which will be charged, it has been fairly said that good professional advice can save the equivalent of the fees in the amount of time and aggravation that would otherwise be expended by a member of the office.

Legislation relevant to smaller offices

Among many other things, professional advisers will be concerned with aspects of legislation affecting the smaller office. Some of this has already been referred to briefly.

The Town and Country Planning Act 1971. This Act regulates, among other matters, the development of all space intended for office use. Both central and local government seek to balance the conflicting environmental and economic demands of each area. This is done statutorily by requiring information to be given to them on all proposals for development by means of formal 'Planning Applications'; reviewing this information against the planning policies agreed for the area, and then pronouncing whether or not the proposal is acceptable. (Many people confuse this process with the requirements of the Building Regulations with which it is totally unconnected: see below.)

Planning Applications and Permissions are required for all new office building; for conversions of premises from another usage to office use and for extensions to existing office premises, before any building or other work may proceed. Planning Applications are made in two stages on the basis of standard applications forms which are provided by the local planning authority. The first stage, consisting of an 'outline' application, requires statements on the general intention of the proposal including location, gross floor area, ownership and present usage, all of which can be given without the need for design drawings (save a location plan). If the planning authority approves the principle, a second 'full' application is then required to be considered and approved before development can begin. This second application must be accompanied by design drawings explaining the proposals in detail.

If an architect has been commissioned, these matters come within his purview, and designs by him will form the basis of the application for full planning permission. However, the process of determining whether or not a straightforward proposal will be acceptable in principle to the planning authority can be carried out by direct consultation between the planners and the developer/owner himself, furthered by an outline application. This is not recommended where the planning policies of an area are 'sensitive', for instance in conservation areas, when the advice of a professional should be sought.

In specified parts of the country, a proposal to develop offices over 2788m² (30,000ft²) in floor area, must first be granted an Office Development Permit (ODP) from the Department of the Environment, without which a planning application will not be considered. If an ODP is refused by the Department no appeal against the Authority is possible. ODP's are required for the rebuilding of old offices as well as for entirely new developments. All planning applications are considered by committees of local government, usually advised by their planning officers. The processing of planning applications and permissions is therefore not a fast one: experience suggests that any application will take between four and eight weeks to process, depending partly on the dates of committee meetings. This time can be very significant in assessing a programme for office change, and is usually under-estimated. When planning applications are rejected, the applicant may appeal to the Secretary of State for the Environment: this process is invariably very long and arduous.

Many small businesses start in a suburban back room and the hard-working proprietor often worries about the attitude of the planning authority. For this to offend against the Planning Acts, it would need to be shown that there has been a 'material' change of use from a house to an office. This could not be sensibly argued where for instance an accountant was using one, or even two, rooms of his house, providing that their purpose remained ancillary to residential use. Expansion into several rooms would certainly be frowned on and then the planning officer would consider serving an enforcement notice insisting that the property be used for its proper purpose. The average planning officer is usually sympathetic to the one man band which is blossoming and, in my experience, will turn a blind eye providing there is a conscientious effort in hand to find appropriate premises within a reasonable time. It is best to speak frankly and directly to the planning officer about these problems and, in many cases, he will give helpful advice.

Building Acts and Regulations. In principle these set out rules for the building standards to be achieved in all buildings regardless of size and purpose. In England and Wales this is by means of controls imposed by the Building Regulations 1972 (as an instrument of the Public Health Acts 1936 and 1961). In Scotland, the Building Standards (Scotland) (Consolidated) Regulations 1971 have the same purpose. Some Local Acts supplement Building Regulations in marginal ways and in Inner London all construction is controlled by the distinct, and very comprehensive, London Building Act and Byelaws. In all these cases, the Acts and Regulations are concerned not only with the stability or specification of construction, but also with the way in which these affect the safety and environment of those who occupy the buildings. For instance, the Building Regulations are specific on constructional matters affecting safety in fire both in construction and means of escape, in thermal and sound insulation and in refuse disposal and drainage.

Formal application to, and approval by, the local authority responsible for administering the particular controls, accompanied by constructional drawings, specifications and calculations, is necessary for all building works, other than repairs, before works may commence. These must be formally approved by officers of the authority before any construction begins. During construction, building inspectors or district surveyors (the latter in Inner London) will inspect to see that the approved constructional design proposals are being followed and to ensure that when modifications to these are necessary (as with conversions) the same standards are applied.

Building inspectors are specially qualified persons who are responsible for maintaining constructional standards. They are not under any obligation to propose or design constructional details nor are they, in any sense, supervisors of building progress. These are the jobs of the professional adviser to the developer. Nor are Building Inspectors concerned with visual appearance or office planning so that their demand for a particular constructional standard to be adopted may well run counter to some favoured visual aspect of the design (for instance, the reduction of glass sizes in a door which they require to have a certain fire resistance). For these reasons, it is sensible to entrust negotiations concerning Building Regulations at all stages of development to the hands of a professional.

All Building Acts and Regulations incorporate minimum provisions for standards of fire escape. In the case of the Building Regulations, a BS Code of Practice (CP 3 Chap IV Part 3 1968) is 'deemed to satisfy' this provision, and is typical of the criteria applied to fire escape. The Code is too lengthy to summarise easily but deals with matters of such importance to life and limb that it should accompany the Offices Act (see below) as compulsory reading for all office proprietors.

Among other criteria given, the following subjects are covered in the Code: safe maximum escape travel distances for various circumstances; requirements for the positioning, widths, lighting and ventilation of staircases; widths of doorways and corridors; the fire resistance of doors, service ducts, partitions, staircase enclosures, storage accommodation, equipment rooms; methods of fire warning and fire fighting equipment. Very few offices are not affected in some way by this Code, and the smaller office in rented or older accommodation is often more at risk from fire than are larger organisations.

The Offices, Shops and Railway Premises Act 1963 (generally referred to as 'the Offices Act'). This Act is complementary to the Building Acts and Regulations and the standards of the latter are normally accepted as meeting its requirements. It sets down environmental space and safety standards for all office space (and other space not effectively covered by existing legislation). Specifically it deals with cleanliness, overcrowding, temperature levels, ventilation and lighting, lavatories, eating and sitting facilities, clothing accommodation, first aid and safety.

Other immediately relevant points required from an office proprietor by the Offices Act are, for instance, in the provision of first aid boxes and wall thermometers and a tabulated list shows the responsibilities of the building owner and of the occupiers in satisfying different parts of the Act. A most useful general guide to the Offices Act is published by HMSO which covers all these matters in simple language and is strongly recommended.

Originally requirements for fire precautions were also included in the Offices Act but in early 1977 these were incorporated into the 1971 Fire Precautions Act (by means of the enabling legislation of the Health and Safety at Work Act 1974 – see later). The principal change which resulted from this was that the local Fire Authority now assumes total responsibility for enforcing fire regulations which was previously the role of Building Inspectors.

An important point to note is that premises granted a fire certificate under the 1961 or 1963 acts, or erected with a permission under building regulations, cannot be required to carry out further alterations under the new act, unless there is a material change of use.

It is important to note that the Fire Precautions require there to be adequate means of escape and free passage to these; that fire exits must be capable of being unlocked or unfastened from the inside and be clearly marked, that there must be an effective way of sounding an alarm, holding fire drills and providing fire fighting equipment. They further require that where more than 20 people are employed or where 10 people are employed other than on the ground floor, such offices be inspected and approved by the local fire authority by means of a formal fire certificate. The Building Regulations are very specific about the fire worthiness of construction and means of escape so that in conjunction with the Fire Precautions Act, the two pieces of legislation are most effective in covering all matters affecting safety from fire. When an overlap or gap does occur in fire safety matters, consultation between the local fire officer and the building inspector will automatically take place, assuming formal applications have been properly made.

Health and Safety at Work Act 1974. This relatively recent legislation is in effect an enabling Act which permits the unification of various aspects of the building control legislation where this proves necessary. Local authorities are responsible for its enforcement. But the Act generally emphasises the responsibility upon every employer to maintain the work environment under his control in a condition which is 'safe, without risks to health' and 'adequate as regards facilities and arrangements' for his employees' welfare. An employer can also be required to prepare 'a written statement of his general policy' in these matters and bring it to the notice of his employees. A series of leaflets on the Act are issued by the Health and Safety Commission and are available from the Health and Safety Executive. It therefore has potentially extensive powers beyond those matters affecting safety covered by legislation described above. For instance the Act can be interpreted as having special application to the equipment, machinery and furniture chosen for use in an office and the appropriate care necessary in this choice.

Landlord and Tenant Acts 1927 and 1954: the main purpose of these Acts as they relate to business tenancies is twofold: first to provide for compensation to a tenant at the end of his tenancy in respect of any beneficial improvements to the property carried out with the agreement of the landlord. Secondly, to provide a measure of security of tenure at a reasonable rent. This legislation is too complex for satisfactory condensation, so that the reader should seek the advice of a solicitor on specific matters. However, the most relevant provisions of the two Acts are summarised below.

A tenant cannot ask for compensation for improvements if such improvements were made because of a contractual obligation, because it is then assumed that they were done in return for a concession, such as a lower rent. Formal notice must be given to a landlord (and any superior landlord) of an intention to carry out improvements accompanied by drawings, and specification. The Landlord has then three options: first to carry out the work himself and increase the rent appropriately; second, to reach an agreement with the tenant as to the work to be carried out by the tenant; and third, to object, in which case the tenant can apply to the Court for a certificate entitling him

to carry out the work. The Act lays down statutory procedures for obtaining a certificate from the landlord, or the court, confirming execution of the improvement and relative to the award of the compensation at the end of the tenancy. A basic consideration is that the improvements must result in a net addition to the value of the property, as a whole.

Under the 1954 Act (as amended by the Law of Property Act 1969), a tenancy shall not end until it is terminated, either by the tenant, or in two other ways, as follows.

First, by means of a landlord's notice to terminate, which is only valid if given not less than six months and not more than 12 months before the intended termination date. It must also indicate whether and on what grounds he would oppose a new tenancy agreement. When the tenant receives this notice to terminate, he must reply within two months saying either that he will give up possession or that he wishes to continue. He may then apply to the Court for a new tenancy not less than two months and not more than four months after receiving the termination notice.

Second, by the tenant's request for a new tenancy, which must be made to the landlord not less than six and not more than 12 months before the termination date. It must be in a prescribed form, setting out the property to be let, the rent proposed and the terms, including duration. The landlord cannot then terminate but must tell the tenant of any objections within two months to avoid the assumption that he agrees to an extension on the terms

proposed. The tenant may then, not less than two, and not more than four months after his original notice, apply to the Court for a new tenancy to be granted, providing he has already sent notice disagreeing with the landlord's objections. The Court must make an Order granting a new tenancy unless the landlord successfully objects on any of the grounds specified in the Act, ie:

1 That the tenant has failed to comply with his obligations to repair and maintain the property.
2 That the tenant has persistently delayed payment of rent.
3 That other substantial breaches or misuse of the premises by the tenant have occurred.
4 That the landlord has offered suitable alternative accommodation.
5 That the landlord may expect to obtain a higher rent by letting the property as a whole and therefore requires possession of the tenancy.
6 That the landlord intends to demolish or reconstruct the premises.
7 That the landlord wants the premises for his own business.

If a new tenancy is agreed then it must not exceed 14 years and there are provisions for assessment of a fair rent. If a new tenancy is refused for a reason not involving fault by the tenant but with benefit to the landlord, then compensation for disturbance is due to the tenant equivalent to the rateable value (or twice this if the tenant has been in occupation for over 14 years). Contracting out of such compensation is allowed to the landlord where business occupation has been for a period of less than five years.

Acknowledgements

The author and publishers are grateful to the following individuals and organisations for their help during the preparation of this book.
D. F. Calow, Solicitor; Business Computers Limited; Eric Fordham of *Business Equipment Digest*; Cyril Pocock of Norman Alexander and Co, Accountants; Anne Benson; Colin Izzard of R. W. Gregory and Partners, Consulting Engineers; Trevor Clayden of Sturt and Tivendale; John Wilson-Wright of Nigel Rose and Partners, Quantity Surveyors; and to those listed below for illustrations.

PAGE	ARCHITECT/DESIGNER	CLIENT/MANUFACTURER	PHOTOGRAPH
15	Clifford Wearden and Associates		
16 top left	Alan Turville FSIAD	Hille International Ltd	
top right		Mines and West Ltd	
bottom	Holder and Mathias Partnership	Office Cleaning Services Ltd	Terence Soames (Cardiff) Ltd
17	Building Design Partnership	William Eaves and Co Ltd	Roger Park
19		Carson Office Furniture Ltd	
24	Alan Turville FSIAD	Hille International Ltd	
27	Geoffrey Salmon, Speed Associates	THM Ltd	Henk Snoek
33 bottom	Peter Bell and Partners		Valerie Allen
38 top left		Drugasar Ltd	
top right		Storad Ltd	
bottom left		Acoustics and Envirometrics Ltd	
bottom right		Dewey Waters and Co Ltd	
42 top	Holder and Mathias Partnership	Office Cleaning Services Ltd	Terence Soames (Cardiff) Ltd
bottom	Geoffrey Salmon, Speed Associates	Slough Estates Ltd	Henk Snoek
43 bottom	John Harris	London Brick Co	Henk Snoek
44		Concorde Lighting International	
45	Michell and Partners	Gillett Brothers Discount Ltd	Colin Westwood
46 left	Alan Turville FSIAD	Hille International Ltd	
centre and right		J. A. Hewetson and Co Ltd	
47 top	Clifford Wearden and Associates	Power Centre Co Ltd	
bottom		Durford Fire Engineering Ltd	
49 left and centre			Post Office
right		Shipton Telstor Ltd	
50			Post Office
51 top			Post Office
bottom		STC Audio Division	
53	Howell, Killick, Partridge and Amis		Brecht-Einzig Ltd

54	Geoffrey Salmon, Speed Associates	Kodak Ltd	Christine Ottewill/Henk Snoek
55	John Harris	London Brick Co	Christine Ottewill/Henk Snoek
56	Dennis Lennon	J. Sainsbury	Architectural Review
57	Michell and Partners	Gillett Brothers Discount Ltd	Colin Westwood
60		Common Aim Ltd	
62 top left		Heuga Vil Ltd	
top right		Cimex Ltd	
bottom		Cape Boards and Panels Ltd	
63		Rockwool Company (UK) Ltd	
64	Geoffrey Salmon, Speed Associates		John Burrell
65 top		R. Howick and Co Ltd	
bottom		Roneo-Vickers Partitions Ltd	
67	Baxton Clark and Paul	Claben Ltd	
68		Arenson International Ltd	Henk Snoek
70 top		Parker Knoll Ltd	
bottom		Mines and West Ltd	
71 left		Ryman Contracts	
right		Mines and West Ltd	
72 left		Herman Miller International	Henk Snoek
right		Ryman Contracts	
75	Jan Jacobs	Gispen Metal Works/	
		Ryman Contracts	
76	Alan Turville FSIAD	Hille International Ltd	
77 top		Carson Office Furniture Ltd	
bottom		Lucas Furniture	
78 top		Herman Miller International	
bottom		Carson Office Furniture	Dennis Hooker
79 top		Meredew	Bill Richmond
bottom		Intercraft	Mann Brothers
80 top		NIPU (UK) Ltd	
bottom	Ray Leigh	Gordon Russell Ltd	
81	Trevor Chinn	Gordon Russell Ltd	
84 top		Ryman Contracts	Dennis Hooker
bottom		Arenson International Ltd	
85		CAPS Microfilm Ltd	John Maltby
87		Philips Electrical Ltd	
		Business Equipment Division	
89		IBM (UK) Ltd	
90		Radio Shack	
90		Oyez Reprographics	
95	Michell and partners	Gillett Brothers Discount Ltd	Colin Westwood
96	A. Hawksworth	JCB Credit Ltd	
97	Mellersh and Harding		Christine Ottewill/Henk Snoek
101			Architect's Journal
102	Rock Townsend Architects	Barley Mow Workspace	
103	Holder and Mathias Partnership	Office Cleaning Services Ltd	Terence Soams (Cardiff) Ltd